MCAT

Essentials

1

MCAT

Essentials

Daniel Roth

B.S. in Microbiology and Immunology

McGill University

Class of 1997

Montreal, Quebec

Williams & Wilkins

A WAVERLY COMPANY

BALTIMORE • PHILADELPHIA • LONDON • PARIS • BANGKOK
BUENOS AIRES • HONG KONG • MUNICH • SYDNEY • TOKYO • WROCLAW

Editor: Elizabeth A. Nieginski
Development Editor: Lisa Kiesel
Manager, Development Editing: Julie Scardiglia
Managing Editor: Amy Dinkel
Marketing Manager: Chris Brenchley
Production Coordinator: Danielle Hagan
Designer: Karen S. Klinedinst
Illustrator: Chansky, Inc.
Cover Designer: Graphic World, Inc.
Typesetter: University Graphics, Inc.
Printer/Binder: Mack Printing Group

351 West Camden Street
Baltimore, Maryland 21201-2436 USA

Rose Tree Corporate Center
1400 North Providence Road
Building II, Suite 5025
Media, Pennsylvania 19063-2043 USA

A portion of the author's proceeds will be directed toward the funding of aplastic anemia research.

Printed in the United States of America

First Edition,

Library of Congress Cataloging-in-Publication Data

Roth, Daniel (Daniel Eliot), 1975–
    MCAT essentials / Daniel Roth.—1st ed. — p.   cm.
    ISBN 0-683-30105-5
    1. Medical colleges United States—Entrance examinations—Study guides.   I. Title.
R838.5.R68   1998
610'.71'173—dc21   97–1663
                                                                      CIP

The publishers have made every effort to trace the copyright holders for borrowed material. If they have inadvertently overlooked any, they will be pleased to make the necessary arrangements at the first opportunity.

To purchase additional copies of this book, call our customer service department at **(800) 638-0672** or fax orders to **(800) 447-8438.** For other book services, including chapter reprints and large quantity sales, ask for the Special Sales department.

Canadian customers should call **(800) 665-1148,** or fax **(800) 665-0103.** For all other calls originating outside of the United States, please call **(410) 528-4223** or fax us at **(410) 528-8550.**

Visit *Williams & Wilkins on the Internet:* **http://www.wwilkins.com** or contact our customer service department at **custserv@ wwilkins.com.** Williams & Wilkins customer service representatives are available from 8:30 am to 6:00 pm, EST, Monday through Friday, for telephone access.

97 98 99 00
1 2 3 4 5 6 7 8 9 10

To Mom and Dad

Contents

Preface

MCAT Essentials is the only available stand-alone compilation of scientific terms and concepts relevant to the Medical College Admission Test (MCAT). More than 1000 concise, detailed definitions provide essential information in the areas of biology, organic chemistry, general chemistry, and physics. The glossary is preceded by recommended study techniques, exam day pointers, and a brief discussion of the nonscience sections of the MCAT. Supplementary tables, diagrams, and equations further illustrate crucial concepts tested on the MCAT.

Written by a fellow student who has personally faced the challenge that now lies before you, *MCAT Essentials* is designed to be with you from the day you decide to take the MCAT plunge to the day you finally write the test. Although *MCAT Essentials* provides an abundance of information and a clear framework to conveniently organize your MCAT study strategy, it is not intended to replace other study materials. Rather, it whould be treated as a comprehensive reference and review manual to accompany you throughout your MCAT preparations.

I hope that you find *MCAT Essentials* to be a constructive and useful tool, and wish you the best of luck in your preparations. Remember, don't let the rough times get you feeling down, nor the good times get you feeling too overconfident. Just relax, study hard, make the most of every minute, and don't forget your *MCAT Essentials*!

Acknowledgments

I am indebted to Lisa Kiesel, Associate Development Editor, for her outstanding efforts throughout the preparation of this book. Many others at Williams & Wilkins, including Julie Scardiglia, Amy Dinkel, and Danielle Hagan, also played key roles. Special thanks to Matthew Chansky for the superb artwork, and to Elizabeth Nieginski, Senior Acquisitions Editor. The invaluable expert reviews by Dr. Harry A. Kiesel and Dr. Frank Scardiglia ensured the accuracy and clarity of the text and figures.

I would also like to acknowledge the constant support of my family and friends; particular thanks to my sister Leah, who drafted many of the illustrations, and Barry Pakes, for his review of the original manuscript. Finally, thank you to Catherine Parry at the University of Calgary Medical Bookstore and Adriana Gabriel at the McGill University Bookstore for all of their encouragement.

Tips for Using *MCAT Essentials*

In addition to comprehensive definitions, *MCAT Essentials* includes several features to enhance your understanding of the defined terms:

- Bolded terms in definitions are defined elsewhere in the glossary. If you do not confidently understand a bolded word, look it up! By starting with a single term, you can work your way through a number of related terms to get a more complete picture of the topic.
- "See also" and "Compare to" at the end of definitions refer the reader to related terms.
- Special notes provide supplementary information about a word or concept related to the definition.

To confirm your understanding of a term, try to cover a definition and either recite it verbally or write it down before looking at it. Also, take the time to look up terms for which the meaning may already seem obvious to you. You will be surprised at how much depth can be added to your understanding of a concept.

If you have any suggestions or corrections, please visit The Science of Review[TM] home page at http://www.wwilkins.com/sor.

PREPARING FOR THE MCAT

The following tips are based on my own recent MCAT experience, so accept them as flexible and adaptable strategies to fit into your own plan for successful MCAT preparation.

WHAT TO SPEND YOUR MONEY ON

As you may have already discovered, taking the MCAT can be an incredibly expensive venture (as if you needed another reason to dislike it!). In addition to the fees required by the AAMC, bookshelves full of manuals, videos, diskettes, and CD-ROMS tempt you to dig deeper into your pockets. Spend as you see fit, but if you would like to limit your purchases, here are some recommendations:

1. Purchase one of the thick, all-encompassing MCAT preparation books. Most of the popular choices include a detailed description of the content and organization of the MCAT, a review of the science material, information covering the skills and methods required for the Verbal Reasoning and Writing Sample sections of the test, and practice questions or exams.
2. Get the official AAMC *MCAT Student Manual, MCAT Practice Test II and Sample Items,* and *MCAT Practice Test III.* These are the only sources of actual MCATs from previous years.
3. I do not recommend spending large sums of money on a commercial preparation course. Unless you need an external source of motivation to study, these classes are overly expensive and largely unnecessary. The AAMC's annual *MCAT Announcement* is right on in suggesting that the courses do not give you any benefits other than the extra time devoted to studying.

HOW TO MAKE THE BEST OUT OF YOUR STUDY TIME

1. **EMPHASIZE GENERAL UNDERSTANDING OVER SPECIFIC MEMORIZATION.** You will be far better off if you are familiar with the general ideas relating to a large number of topics rather than numerous details regarding only a handful of concepts. The key to MCAT success is eliminating the element of surprise. The passage before each set of test questions provides you with most of the details that are required to solve the problems. What you need to come equipped with is a confident familiarity with the concepts and terms to allow you to efficiently assess the passage details and appropriately fit them into the knowledge base you have built during test preparation.
2. **Make sure you have at least a basic knowledge of every concept that may appear on the MCAT.** Regular use of *MCAT Essentials* will familiarize you with the terminology and concepts in the science sections of the MCAT. Come exam day, an effortless comprehension of the terms in passages and questions will prevent you from wasting valuable time that you can use to solve the given problems.
3. **Become comfortable with the use of scientific terminology in contexts where its actual meaning may not be obvious.** For example, the expression, "work done on a wooden crate,"

should be immediately recognized as a reference to an external force applied to the crate, which causes it to undergo a particular displacement.

4. **Do not exclusively study one science section before moving on to the next.** Do not immerse yourself in chemistry for two straight weeks, then biology, and then physics. Your study strategy should always reflect the fact that the MCAT emphasizes the integration of concepts from all of the disciplines.

5. **Make sure you can apply single concepts to several different disciplines.** For example, adapt your understanding of the potential difference across an electrical device to explain the membrane potential in a neuron, or use the principles of optics (e.g., refraction) to understand the function of the lens in the eye.

6. **Never use a calculator while you study.** You will not have the luxury of using a calculator during the MCAT, so do not spoil yourself during MCAT preparation.

7. **Leave yourself plenty of time to prepare for the MCAT.** Only you can be the judge of how much time you will need to study; however, this will probably be one of the longest stretches of studying you ever do for one exam, so use it to your advantage. Never stop studying a concept until you are confident that you understand it. There is always tomorrow to move on to the next topic.

8. **Do not overstudy.** Particularly if you are taking the August MCAT, it is not a good idea to make MCAT studying your only major activity for 3 months. Excessive studying often leads to inefficient use of time. In addition, your motivation will likely diminish as you get progressively bored with studying what essentially amounts to a large but limited quantity of information.

9. **Plan regular reviews.** Use at least one weekly study session to specifically go over everything you taught yourself the previous week. Repeat practice questions to identify weaknesses as well as to boost your confidence with what you already know.

10. **Do not try to learn *new* concepts by looking up the relevant terms in *MCAT Essentials*.** This book is primarily intended for reference and review of topics that you have previously learned using old lecture notes, textbooks, and other traditional resources.

11. **Use more than one resource when teaching yourself a new scientific concept.** Professors, textbooks, and MCAT review books all emphasize different points, so provide yourself with a good balance of resources. Using a variety of resources will also reveal their individual strengths and weaknesses; select only the best explanations and examples from each resource as you compile your personal set of study notes. I suggest piecing together your own set of definitions of terms and concepts, then compare them to the definitions in *MCAT Essentials* to see what you are missing (or what I may have missed!).

HOW TO PREPARE FOR THE NONSCIENCE SECTIONS OF THE MCAT

A thorough scientific knowledge is not sufficient to get you successfully through the MCAT. The Verbal Reasoning and Writing Sample sections specifically test your critical and analytical reasoning abilities as well as your ability to write clearly and effectively. Studying for these sections of the test is just as important as studying the basic sciences. In fact, depending on your strengths and weaknesses, you may need to put more effort into the nonscience than the science sections.

For many people, the greatest challenge is simply figuring out how to prepare for these language-based components. In general, you need to have more discipline than you do when studying the sciences, simply because your means of self-evaluation are less obvious. However, as abstract as these sections may seem, there is definitely some order behind the apparent chaos. The more practice you give yourself, the more trends and patterns you will see in the types of questions and passages found on the MCAT. This means fewer surprises the day of the exam, giving you more time to spend where it counts.

The large MCAT review books usually contain chapters devoted to the Verbal Reasoning and Writing Sample sections. There are also library shelves full of books on how to improve your own literary style. Just remember that practice is the key to doing well on the Verbal Reasoning and Writing Sample components of the MCAT. The following are some of my own suggestions designed to put you on the right track.

Verbal Reasoning

TEST-TAKING STRATEGIES

For the Verbal Reasoning section of the test, you will be required to read a short passage, understand everything the author attempted to express, and answer several multiple-choice questions accordingly, all within a very tight time limit (approximately 9 minutes per passage). For optimum comprehension and time efficiency, I suggest that you skim the passage, read the questions, read the passage in detail, and then go back and answer the questions.

Skim the Passage (approximately 30 seconds)
Skimming refers to reading the passage title, the first sentence of every paragraph, and the last couple of sentences of the passage. This may seem cold and calculated, but it should give you an idea of the subject at hand and allow you to get your mind focused.

Read the Questions (approximately 30 seconds)
This will give you a framework to use when you read the passage in detail. Do not read the answer choices yet; you simply do not have time to waste.

Read the Passage in Detail (approximately 3½ minutes)
Make sure that you are actively involved in the reading process: underline or circle key terms, draw arrows to link important ideas, and make notes in the margins to keep track of your impressions. As you read, try to answer the following questions: What is the bigger picture? What are the author's purpose, bias, and perspective? If appropriate, what is the opposing side of the issue? It is not necessary to pause to ponder these questions; rather, just keep them in mind as you read.

Answer the Multiple-Choice Questions (approximately 4½ minutes)
Ideally, you read the passage so carefully that you rarely need to look back at it to answer the questions. However, when you do need to reread parts of the passage for clues to the answers, your notes, circles, and arrows should direct your eyes to the relevant place in the text.

ADDITIONAL HINTS

Do not search beyond the passage for facts that are not presented. All of the questions relate directly to the information in the passage. You are not required to have prior knowledge of any particular political, social, cultural, or historical issues. However, it may be helpful to regularly read the newspaper to give yourself the opportunity to identify and analyze the two sides of societal debates. Any amount of effort you can put into building critical reading skills will better prepare you for the MCAT.

Finally, always remember that timing is key. Many people have trouble completing the Verbal Reasoning component. Some people spend too much time searching the passage for the answers, likely because they did not read actively enough in the first place. If you follow the strategy previously discussed (skim the passage, read the questions, read the passage, answer the questions), you will read the questions *before* you read the passage, allowing you to *predict* answers to the questions as you work your way through the passage. Your anticipation of the correct answer should increase the speed at which you eliminate incorrect response choices.

Writing Sample

Each of the two MCAT Writing Samples begins with a given statement of opinion. You are required to:

1. **Explain** what is written
2. Give appropriate examples to **support** the statement
3. Present a situation or idea that contradicts or otherwise **argues** against the validity of the statement
4. **Resolve** the conflict between the given opinion and the opposition you have provided

Remember to always use specific examples to support general statements. Discuss current events, historical facts, or personal ordeals to illustrate every idea that you put forth.

You can easily practice by making up your own statements of opinion. The following are just a few examples of the many types of statements you could use to practice your essay writing:

- *Government representatives are bound to the platforms they were elected on. Any deviation from this ideal is contrary to democratic values.*
- *Personal satisfaction comes not from improving the actions of oneself, but from changing the behavior of others.*
- *The common good is only achieved at the expense of the good of the common people.*

Be aware of the time limit, because you have only 30 minutes for each essay on the MCAT. Make sure you leave yourself enough time to wrap up. If there are 30 seconds left and you are still in the body of the essay (hopefully this will not happen), force yourself to stop, skip to the end, and conclude. Anything coherent that brings some kind of closure to the ideas within your piece of writing will be beneficial.

After you complete a practice essay, ask a friend, family member, or professor to look over your writing. They should assess the essay holistically, but should also review your mechanics, word choice, sentence structure, relevance of the examples, and strength of the argumentation. You should also read your essay again a day or two after writing it. If you find yourself disappointed with what you see, rewrite the essay (within the 30 minute time limit, of course) and evaluate your progress.

WHAT TO DO ON EXAM DAY

The exam day is a tiring and gruelling experience for which you need to be both physically and mentally prepared. Although I am sure you are familiar with the finer points of taking exams, here are some MCAT-specific pointers to add to your arsenal.

1. **Timing is key.** If you find yourself stumped, move on to the next question without delay. Every question is worth the same number of points and there is no penalty for guessing; therefore, it is better to guess on a question to which you do not know the answer than to waste time on it, forcing yourself to miss a question at the end of the exam to which you may have known the answer if you had had time to answer it.

2. **Do not study during the breaks.** You have been studying for weeks; ten minutes cannot possibly help, especially on a day when you are already working yourself to the bone. Rather, use the time to rest, grab something to drink, and relax yourself in preparation for the next section.

3. **Do not compare answers with other people during the breaks.** Wait until you are finished the test, when the pressure is off, to discuss answers.

4. **Eat well, exercise, and get plenty of sleep** during the days preceding the exam (some sound advice from my mom!).

A

Abductor. Any **muscle** that moves a limb away from the midline of the body.

> *Compare to* **adductor**

Absolute configuration. The true, three-dimensional arrangement of chemical groups about a **chiral center**. More specifically, it is the designation of the **chirality**, or handedness, of the **molecule**. The designation of the molecule as (R) or (S) is based on the following rules *(Figure 1)*.

1. Assign the four groups an order of priority according to the sequence rules of the **Cahn-Ingold-Prelog nomenclature system**.
2. Adjust the molecule so that the group with the lowest priority faces away from the observer (i.e., into the page).
3. Start from the group of highest priority and draw a curved arrow in the direction of decreasing priority. Consider only the three highest priority groups when drawing the arrow (i.e., the lowest priority group has no effect on the direction of the arrow).
4. If the arrow is clockwise , the **configuration** is (R); if the arrow is counterclockwise, the configuration is (S).

> *See also* **Cahn-Ingold-Prelog nomenclature system, enantiomer, Fischer projection**
> *Compare to* **conformation, relative configuration**

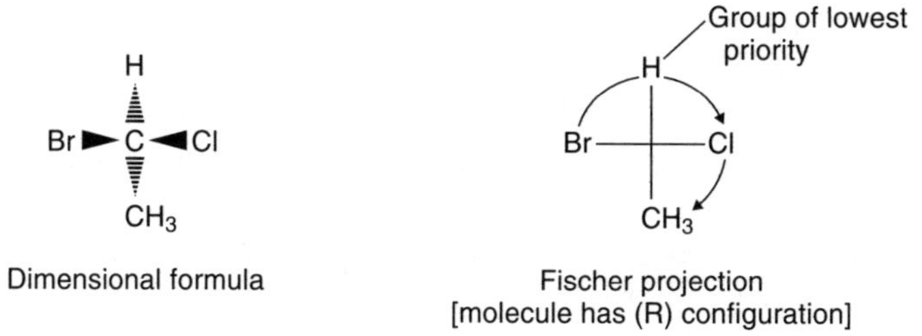

Dimensional formula

Fischer projection
[molecule has (R) configuration]

Figure 1. Absolute configuration

Absorption spectrum. The **frequencies** of **electromagnetic radiation** that are most readily absorbed by an **atom** of a specific **element**. An atom can only absorb **photons** of energies that correspond to its available atomic **energy** levels. The atom's **electrons** capture these photons and harness the energy by boosting themselves to the higher available energy levels, at which point they are in an **excited state**. The color of a substance corresponds to the **wavelengths** of light that are not in its absorption spectrum (i.e., those that are reflected or transmitted by the atoms).

Acceleration. The change in **velocity** as a function of time; acceleration is a **vector**. Average acceleration (a) is measured as the average change in velocity (Δv) during a defined time interval (Δt):

$$a = \frac{\Delta v}{\Delta t}$$

✔ Calculations involving instantaneous acceleration are not required to solve problems on the MCAT.

Accommodation, visual. An adaptive change in the shape of the **lens** of the eye between a moderate and a very **convex lens**. Accommodation allows the eye to focus on objects at variable distances.

Acetal. An organic **molecule** that contains two **ether** groups on the same carbon **atom**. It is formed by the **nucleophilic addition** of two **alcohol** molecules to an **aldehyde** or **ketone**, with the loss of water *(Figure 2)*. This reaction is important in the formation of **glycosidic bonds**.

See also **hemiacetal, ketone**

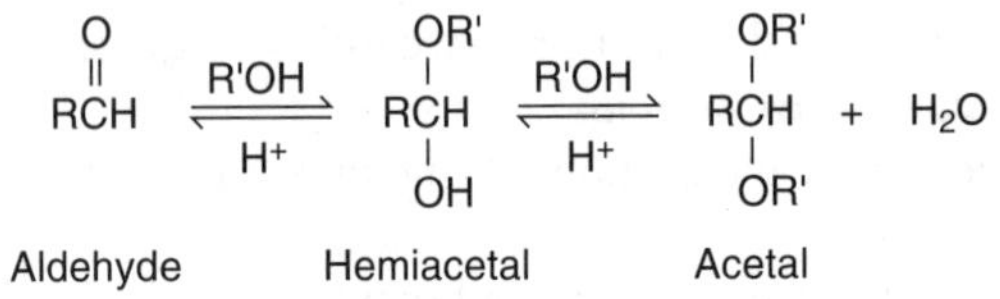

$$\underset{\text{Aldehyde}}{\overset{\displaystyle \overset{O}{\underset{\|}{}}}{RCH}} \xrightleftharpoons[\text{H}^+]{\text{R'OH}} \underset{\text{Hemiacetal}}{\overset{OR'}{\underset{OH}{RCH}}} \xrightleftharpoons[\text{H}^+]{\text{R'OH}} \underset{\text{Acetal}}{\overset{OR'}{\underset{OR'}{RCH}}} + H_2O$$

Figure 2. Acetal formation

Acetylcholine. A chemical **neurotransmitter** responsible for the passing of **nerve impulses** across all **synapses** in the **parasympathetic nervous system**, certain synapses in the **sympathetic nervous system**, and **neuromuscular junctions**. A **neuron** that secretes acetylcholine is said to be cholinergic.

Compare to **noradrenaline**

Acetylcholinesterase. The **enzyme** that catalyzes the **hydrolysis** of **acetylcholine** at cholinergic **synapses**, which is a reaction that helps to end the transmission of a **nerve impulse**.

Acid. Any chemical substance that fits into one of the following three definitions.

1. A Brönsted-Lowry acid is a chemical substance that is capable of donating a **proton** to another substance.
2. An Arrhenius acid is an **electrolyte** for which the **cation** is a proton.
3. A Lewis acid is a substance that can accept an **electron** pair (e.g., **electrophiles**).

   ✔ The term acid can also refer to a **solution** with a **pH** less than 7.

Acidic salt. An **electrolyte** for which dissociation reveals that the **cation** is a **weak acid**. An acidic salt is always formed in the reaction between a **strong acid** and a **weak base**. Using NH_4Cl as an example:

Formation:

$$NH_{3(g)} + HCl_{(g)} \rightleftharpoons NH_4Cl_{(aq)}$$

(weak base) + (strong acid) $\rightleftharpoons$ (acidic salt)

Acidic cation dissociation:

$$NH_4^+ + H_2O \rightleftharpoons H_3O^+ + NH_3$$

   ✔ Due to the acidity of the cation, a **solution** containing an acidic salt has a **pH** below 7.

Acidity constant (K_a). The **equilibrium constant** for the reaction between a **weak acid** and water, given by the equation:

$$HA + H_2O \rightleftharpoons A^- + H_3O^+$$

$$K_a = \frac{[A^-][H_3O^+]}{[HA]}$$

Using acetic acid as an example:

$$CH_3COOH + H_2O \rightleftharpoons CH_3COO^- + H_3O^+$$

$$K_a = \frac{[CH_3COO^-][H_3O^+]}{[CH_3COOH]} = 1.8 \times 10^{-5}$$

✔ Acidity constants for **strong acids** are considered to be infinite, indicating complete dissociation in **solution**.

Compare to **basicity constant**

Acrosome. A vesicle that is derived from the **Golgi body** and contained in the **cell** body of a **spermatozoon**. It contains digestive **enzymes** that facilitate penetration of the **ovum**.

Actin. A globular **protein** that is assembled into polymeric **microfilaments** found as structural or contractile **elements** in all **cells**. These "thin filaments" are found in large amounts in **muscle cells**. In the **sarcomere**, they are anchored at the periphery (Z-lines) and transiently bind to **myosin** filaments during **muscle contraction**. Actin is the most abundant protein in many eukaryotic cells.

Action potential (AP). A self-propagating shift of **ions** or charges across a **cell membrane** caused by a transient membrane **depolarization** that is large enough to cause voltage-gated sodium channels to open. The process takes approximately 1–5 ms and is as follows *(Figure 3)*.

1. Depolarization. A stimulus (e.g., **pressure**, chemical activity) at a magnitude of at least the **threshold value** causes a depolarization great enough to briefly open voltage-gated sodium channels in a cell membrane, allowing a localized flood of Na^+ to diffuse *into* the **cell**. Depolarization wipes out the **resting potential** equilibrium. This stage corresponds to the absolute **refractory period**.
2. Repolarization. The resulting reversal of the **membrane potential** causes the sodium channels to close and voltage-gated potassium channels to open, allowing K^+ to diffuse *out* of the cell. During a brief relative refractory period, the membrane potential can drop below the resting potential due to the relative rapidity of the potassium outflow.
3. Resting state. The Na-K-ATPase pump restores the resting potential by pumping *out* Na^+ and pumping *in* K^+. At this point, the membrane is fully capable of sustaining another AP.

✔ In **neurons**, the AP allows the extended travel of **nerve impulses** because the ion shift has a self-amplifying effect (i.e., it creates a small, localized **current** that causes additional sodium channels to open on adjacent regions of the neuronal membrane).

✔ The AP is an all-or-nothing response; its strength depends on the characteristics of the membrane (e.g., diameter) and is independent of the strength of the stimulus that initially triggered the depolarization.

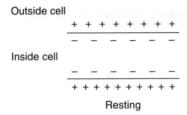

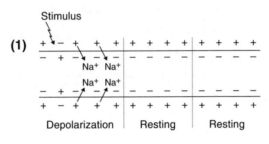

Direction of impulse →

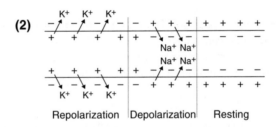

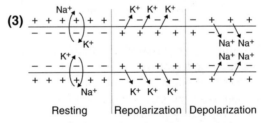

Figure 3. Propagation of an action potential

Activated complex. A molecular **configuration** that is comprised of all the **atoms** involved in a given chemical reaction. It is an unstable, transient species that forms when the reactants acquire the necessary **activation energy**. It exists only in the **activated state** when the **potential energies** of all particles or atoms are at a maximum.

Activated state. The transitional state of a reaction when the **activated complex** is formed. On a plot of **potential energy** versus time of a reaction, the activated state is the point of maximum potential energy (see Appendix B, Figure 3). For products to form, the reactants *must* proceed through the activated state.

Also called transition state

Activation energy (E_a). The difference in **potential energy** between the **activated state** and the **equilibrium state** of the reactants (see Appendix B, Figure 3). In other words, it is the **energy** barrier that must be overcome for a chemical reaction to proceed. The magnitude directly affects the rate of the reaction (i.e., the higher the activation energy, the slower the reaction).

  ✔ An external energy source must supply the reactants with activation energy to form the **activated complex**.

  See also **catalyst, enzyme**

Active site. The specific location on the 3-dimensional surface structure of an **enzyme** or **catalyst** where the **substrate(s)** bind *(Figure 4)*. The substrate often induces the **protein** to change its shape slightly to allow for a tighter, or induced, fit. The substrate-enzyme linkages are often **covalent bonds** between **amino acids** that are placed in close proximity as a result of the induced fit.

  ✔ The active site is where catalysis occurs.

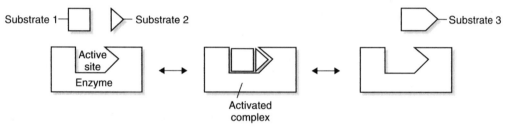

Figure 4. Active site

Active transport. An **energy**-dependent movement of **molecules** or **ions** across a **cell membrane** and against a **concentration** gradient. The mechanism involves **adenosine triphosphate**-dependent channels. Intracellular sodium, potassium, and calcium ion concentrations are commonly regulated by active transport mechanisms.

  Compare to **diffusion, facilitated diffusion**

Addition reaction. A chemical reaction in which an unsaturated **molecule** (i.e., contains either carbon-carbon multiple bonds or carbon-oxygen double bonds) accepts new substituents without losing any substituents in the process.

  See also **electrophilic addition, halogenation, hydration, hydrogenation, hydrohalogenation**
  Compare to **elimination reaction**

Adductor. Any **muscle** that moves a limb toward the midline of the body.

  Compare to **abductor**

Adenosine triphosphate (ATP). The **molecule** that acts as the most common means of transferring **energy** from metabolic reactions to **cell** functions. It is able to play this role because the **covalent bonds** between its **phosphate groups** are easily broken (i.e., have low **activation energies**), yet contain a relatively large amount of energy (approximately 7.3 kcal/mole). When hydrolyzed (broken), the bonds in ATP release a net amount of energy (**exothermic process**) that is greater than the activation energies of most cellular reactions.

✔ If an ATP **hydrolysis** reaction is coupled to an energy-requiring reaction of the cell, the net excess of energy resulting from ATP hydrolysis can be used to supply the activation energy.

✔ Although ATP is constantly being used up in coupled reaction systems, it is continually being formed from adenosine diphosphate (ADP) and organic phosphate as a result of **respiration**, **fermentation**, or photophosphorylation reactions.

Adhesion. An intermolecular attractive force between unlike **molecules** and surfaces with which they are in contact.

Compare to **cohesion**

Adrenal cortex. The outer layer of the adrenal **gland**. When stimulated by **adrenocorticotropic hormone**, it produces **corticosteroids** (e.g., **aldosterone**).

Adrenaline. A **hormone** produced by the **adrenal medulla** that is responsible for the diverse physiologic adaptations known collectively as the "flight-or-fight" response. It also acts as a **neurotransmitter** in terminal sympathetic **synapses**.

Also called epinephrine
See also **sympathetic nervous system**

✔ Recall that terminal synapses are found in target organs.

Adrenal medulla. The inner portion of the adrenal **gland** that primarily secretes **noradrenaline** and **adrenaline**.

Adrenocorticotropic hormone (ACTH). A **hormone** secreted by the **anterior pituitary gland** that stimulates the **adrenal cortex** to produce **corticosteroids**. Because ACTH is a trophic hormone, it also controls and maintains the size of the adrenal gland.

Adsorption. The **adhesion** of **molecules** to the surface of a **solid**.

Adventitia. An outer layer of **connective tissue** that surrounds **organs** such as the **blood vessels**.

Aerobe. An organism that requires oxygen for **metabolism**. In aerobic metabolism, oxygen serves as the final **electron** acceptor in the **electron transport chain**.

Compare to **facultative anaerobe, obligate anaerobe**

Afferent. That which leads toward a particular destination, such as an **organ** (e.g., **blood** flows into the **glomerulus** through the afferent arteriole).

Compare to **efferent**

Albumin. The most abundant blood **protein** that primarily serves to maintain **oncotic pressure** in **capillaries**. It also acts as a nonspecific carrier protein in the **blood**.

Alcohols. **Hydrocarbon** derivatives that have one or more **hydroxyl groups** in place of hydrogen **atoms** [e.g., ethanol *(Figure 5)*]. These compounds are characterized by **hydrogen bonding** in water, **boiling points** much higher than **alkanes**, and solubility in water (if the **hydrophobic** hydrocarbon chain is relatively short).

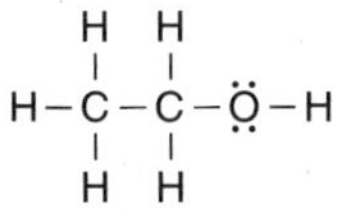

H H
| |
H−C−C−Ö−H
| |
H H

Figure 5. Ethanol

Aldehyde. An organic compound that contains a **carbonyl group** with at least one hydrogen **atom** bond [e.g., acetaldehyde *(Figure 6)*]. These compounds are characterized by polarity of the carbonyl group; higher **boiling points** than nonpolar compounds of similar **molecular weight**, but lower boiling points relative to analogous **alcohols**; and aqueous solubility due to **hydrogen bonding** with water **molecules**.

> *Compare to* **ketone**

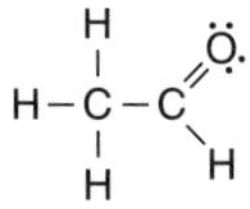

H   Ö.
| ∥
H−C−C
| \
H   H

Figure 6. Acetaldehyde

Aldol condensation, base-catalyzed. The addition of one **aldehyde** to another when treated with a **base** *(Figure 7)*. The product, a β-hydroxy aldehyde, is called an aldol (from *ald*ehyde and alcoh*ol*). The reaction proceeds via the formation of an **enolate ion**.

> *See also* **condensation reaction**

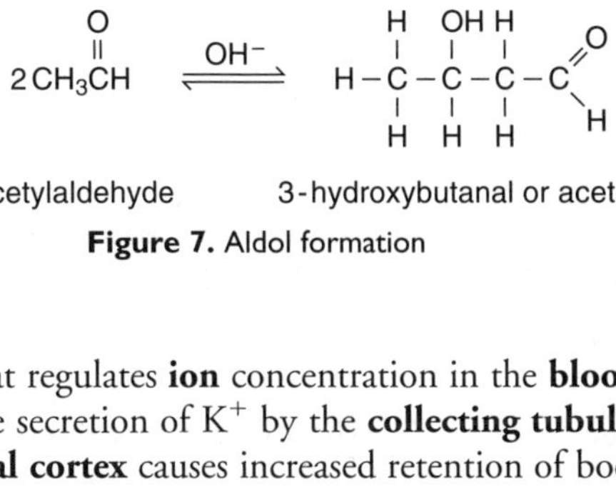

O   H OH H
∥ | | | O
2 CH$_3$CH $\rightleftharpoons$ OH$^-$ H−C−C−C−C
                            | | | \
                            H H H   H

Acetylaldehyde   3-hydroxybutanal or acetaldol

Figure 7. Aldol formation

Aldosterone. A **hormone** that regulates **ion** concentration in the **blood** by stimulating the reabsorption of Na$^+$ and the secretion of K$^+$ by the **collecting tubules**. Increased production of aldosterone by the **adrenal cortex** causes increased retention of body **fluid**.

Alkanes. The class of organic **molecules** that is comprised of the saturated **hydrocarbons**. In these molecules, all carbon **atoms** are sp^3-hybridized [e.g., butane *(Figure 8)*]. Alkanes are characterized by a lack of functional groups; a lack of double or triple bonds; nonpolar, **hydrophobic** interactions; and low **boiling points** (relative to **alcohols** of similar **molecular weight**).

H H H H
| | | |
H−C−C−C−C−H
| | | |
H H H H

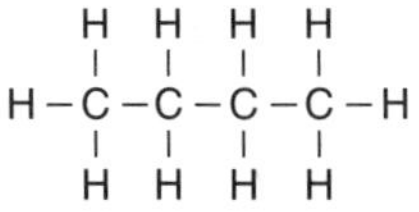

Figure 8. Butane

Alkenes. A class of organic **molecules** that is comprised of unsaturated **hydrocarbons** with at least one double bond between adjacent sp^2-hybridized carbon **atoms** {e.g., ethene [ethylene] *(Figure 9)*}. Alkenes are characterized by a similarity to **alkanes**, very weak polarity, solubility in nonpolar solvents, slightly higher water solubility than corresponding alkanes, and **electron**-donating double bonds.

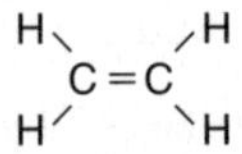

$$
\begin{array}{ccc}
H & & H \\
\diagdown & & \diagup \\
& C = C & \\
\diagup & & \diagdown \\
H & & H
\end{array}
$$

Figure 9. Ethene

Alkyl group (-CH$_3$). The portion of any **alkane** that remains after the removal of a single hydrogen **atom**.

Alkyl radical. An sp^2-hybridized **alkyl group** that contains an unpaired **electron** and is involved in **free-radical substitution reactions**.

Alkynes. A class of organic **molecules** comprised of **hydrocarbons** that contain at least one triple carbon-carbon bond between two sp-hybridized carbon **atoms** {e.g., ethyne [acetylene] *(Figure 10)*}. Alkynes are characterized by a similarity to **alkanes** and **alkenes** and some solubility in water.

$$H - C \equiv C - H$$

Figure 10. Ethyne

Allele. A genetic variant or version of a **gene**. Several different alleles for a given gene often exist in a **population**.

Allele frequency. The proportional occurrence of a particular **allele** among all alleles for a **gene** present in the individuals of a **population**.

> *Compare to* **gene frequency**

Allelic pair. A pair of **genes** in a single **diploid genome** that encode for the same trait. For example, a blue-eye gene on a paternal **chromosome** and a brown-eye gene on a maternal chromosome collectively constitute an allelic pair.

> *See also* **homologous pair**

Allosteric ligands. Regulatory **molecules** (not **substrates**) that bind to an **enzyme** at an allosteric site, which is any location other than the **active site**. This causes a conformational shift in the enzyme structure that positively or negatively effects the catalytic activity of the enzyme. As such, the enzyme can be regulated by **feedback inhibition**.

> ✔ A single enzyme can possess more than one allosteric site.
>
> *Also called* allosteric effectors

Alpha particle. A helium **nucleus** ($^4_2He^{2+}$) that is released from a radioactive **element**. Unstable nuclei that emit alpha particles are said to undergo alpha decay.

Alveoli. Tiny air sacs in the **lungs** that serve as the functional units of the lungs. **Gas** exchange takes place across the membranes of the alveoli, which must be in close proximity to the pulmonary **capillary** bed for the exchange to be efficient.

Amide. A **carboxylic acid** derivative that contains a nitrogen **atom** directly bonded to a **carbonyl group**. Amides can result from a nucleophilic attack of an **amine** on a carbonyl carbon atom. The rigid bond (i.e., resists rotation) that forms between the carbon and nitrogen atoms is generally called an amide bond; however, it is referred to as a **peptide bond** when specifically discussing the link between adjacent **amino acids** in **polypeptides**.

Amine. A nitrogen-containing, **electron**–pair-donating organic **molecule** that can serve as a weak organic **base**. An amine is a derivative of ammonia in which one or more hydrogens are replaced by **alkyl** or **aryl groups**. In this molecule, an sp³-hybridized nitrogen **atom** is bonded to three other atoms or chemical groups with one pair of unshared **valence electrons** in the remaining sp³ orbital. Amines are classified as primary, secondary, or tertiary according to whether one, two, or three alkyl or aryl substituents are bonded to the nitrogen {e.g., trimethylamine [a tertiary amine] *(Figure 11)*}. Amines are characterized by **hydrogen bonding** between the nitrogen and hydrogen atoms (except in tertiary amines); solubility in water (for low **molecular weight** amines); and **boiling points** higher than similar molecular weight **alkanes**, but lower than **alcohols**.

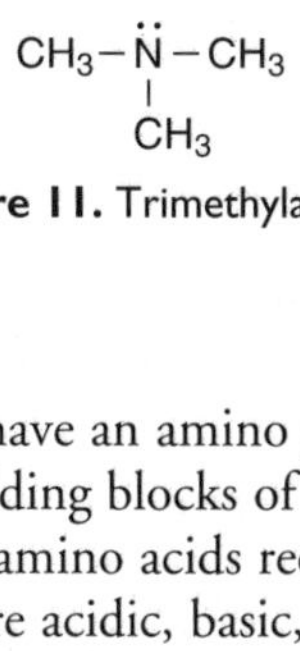

$$CH_3-\overset{\displaystyle ..}{N}-CH_3$$
$$|$$
$$CH_3$$

Figure 11. Trimethylamine

Amino acids. Organic **molecules** that have an amino group ($-NH_2$) and a **carboxyl group** (COOH) and are the monomeric building blocks of **polypeptides**. The general formula is shown in *Figure 12*. The 20 different amino acids required by humans can be grouped according to whether their side chains are acidic, basic, uncharged polar, or nonpolar, which has important consequences for the role of amino acids in **protein** structure.

✔ Amino acids in a polypeptide chain are referred to as residues because they can no longer be considered true amino acids due to the formation of **peptide bonds**.

See also **isoelectric point, zwitterion**

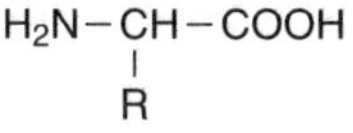

$$H_2N-CH-COOH$$
$$|$$
$$R$$

Figure 12. General structure of an amino acid

Amniocentesis. The removal of a sample of amniotic **fluid** that contains fetal **cells** and can be tested for genetic disorders.

Amnion. The innermost of the extraembryonic membranes that surround the **fetus** in utero. Early in fetal development, the amnion fuses with the **chorion** so that only one membrane surrounds the fetus.

Ampere (A). One ampere equals one **coulomb** per second (C/s). It serves as a unit of **current**.

Ampere's law. A physical law that states that a **magnetic field** is produced by an electric **current** or a changing **electric field** (i.e., a moving charge).

Amplitude (A). The maximum **displacement** of a vibrating body from its equilibrium point. For a **transverse wave**, this translates into the maximum height of a crest or maximum depth of a trough relative to the equilibrium level *(Figure 13)*. The amplitude of a wave can be referred to in terms of its **intensity**.

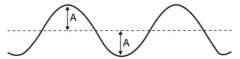

Figure 13. Amplitude. A = amplitude.

Ampulla. An enlargement at the end of each **semicircular duct** that contains hair **cells** that are sensitive to changes in angular **acceleration** caused by rotations of the head.

> *See also* **vestibular system**

Amylase. An **enzyme** that breaks up **polysaccharides** (e.g., **starch**) into **disaccharides**. It is secreted by the salivary **glands** and into the **duodenum** by the **pancreas**.

Anabolism. The metabolic act of building complex **molecules** from simple molecules.

Anaerobe. See **facultative anaerobe, obligate anaerobe**

Anaerobic respiration. **Energy**-yielding metabolic processes that take place in the absence of oxygen (e.g., **glycolysis**).

Analogous structures. Anatomical features of organisms that have common functions but arose from different ancestral structures.

Anaphase. The "third" stage of **mitosis** in which the paired sister **chromatids** migrate away from one another as the **spindle fibers** shorten and pull the **chromosomes** toward opposite poles of the dividing **cell**. In **meiosis**, anaphase I is marked by the separation of **homologous chromosomes** and the migration of the chromosomes toward opposite ends of the cell.

These migrating chromosomes have intact **centromeres**. Anaphase II is similar to the mitotic anaphase.

See also **meiosis, mitosis**
Compare to **interphase, metaphase, prophase, telophase**

Aneuploidy. Having one or more extra, or one or more fewer than the normal number of **chromosomes**. For example, trisomy 21 is the human condition of one extra partial copy of chromosome 21, an aneuploidy that causes Down syndrome.

Angular momentum quantum number (*l*). The component of an **atom's electron config-uration** that defines the **atomic orbital** shape and classifies the subshell.

Anion. An **ion** with a negative charge.

Anode. The **electrode** where **oxidation** occurs. Anodes are negatively charged in **electrochem-ical** or **galvanic cells**, but positively charged in **electrolytic cells**.

Anomers. A pair of **diastereomers** (or **epimers**) that differ only in their **configurations** at carbon "1" [e.g., D-glucose *(Figure 14)*]. Anomers arise as a result of the formation of cyclic **hemiacetals** (e.g., cyclic forms of **monosaccharides**). Carbon "1," referred to as the ano-meric carbon, is derived from the **carbonyl group** of the open-chain **aldehyde**; in the cyclic form, it characteristically bears two oxygen substituents. Carbon "1" becomes a **chiral center** as a result of the hemiacetal-forming cyclization reaction. The orientation of the anomeric **hydroxyl group** determines the relative configuration of the anomer; in the α-anomer, the anomeric OH group is *trans* (down) to the terminal CH_2OH, and in the β-anomer, the ano-meric OH group is *cis* (up) to the terminal CH_2OH.

See also **mutarotation**

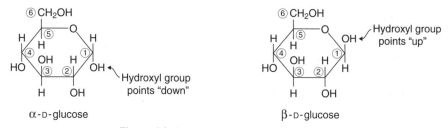

Figure 14. Anomeric forms of glucose

Anterior pituitary gland. See **pituitary gland**

Antibody. A multimeric **protein,** produced by mature **B lymphocytes (plasma cells)**, that specifically binds to an **antigen** to neutralize it or mark it for destruction (e.g., **phagocytosis**, **complement**-mediated **lysis**). Although antibodies have variable binding capacities at the antigen-binding sites, they have relatively common binding specificities at the constant re-gion, which binds substances such as complement and **cell** surface receptors *(Figure 15).*

Also called immunoglobulin

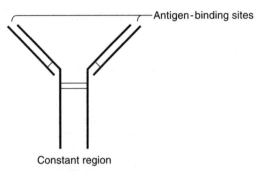

Constant region

Figure 15. Antibody

Anticodon. A sequence of three **nucleotides** on a **transfer ribonucleic acid** that pairs with a specific **codon** of **messenger ribonucleic acid** during **translation** of a **protein**.

Antidiuretic hormone (ADH). See **vasopressin**

Antigen (Ag). Any substance that can be bound by an **antibody**. An antigen is usually, but not always, a foreign substance that enters the body and elicits an **immune response**.

Antinode. A point of maximal **constructive interference** between two **waves** or within a **standing wave**.

Aorta. The large **blood vessel** that carries oxygenated **blood** from the left **ventricle** of the **heart** to the body **tissues**.

Aortic valve. A piece of specialized **heart tissue** that separates the **aorta** and the left **ventricle**.

Aqueous humor. An intraocular **liquid** that fills the space between the **cornea** and the **lens**. It creates **pressure** to maintain the contour of the eyeball.

> *Compare to* **vitreous humor**

Archenteron. The principal **endoderm**-lined cavity in the **gastrula**; it represents the future digestive tract.

Archimedes' principle. States that an object that is completely or partially submerged in a **fluid** experiences an upward **force** equal to the **weight** of the fluid displaced.

> *See also* **buoyant force**

Aromatic compounds. Organic **molecules** that contain cyclic planar structures that are substantially stabilized when **electrons** are delocalized over one or more rings of **atoms (resonance)** [e.g., benzene *(Figure 16)*]. These compounds follow **Huckel's rule**.

> ✔ Benzene does not undergo most of the reactions typical of **alkenes**, yet it is not inert. Under proper conditions, benzene readily undergoes **electrophilic aromatic substitution**.

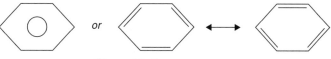

Figure 16. Benzene

Artery. Any thick-walled, elastic **blood vessel** that carries oxygenated **blood** from the **heart** to the body **tissues**.

Artificial selection. The human-controlled process of positively or negatively selecting specific **phenotypes** for further breeding. It is typified by the practice of eugenics.

Compare to **natural selection**

Aryl group. The portion of any **aromatic compound** that remains after the removal of a hydrogen **atom**. It has the ability to act as a chemical substituent.

Atom. The smallest unit of an **element** that can chemically combine with other elements. An atom is electrically neutral; it is composed of an equal number of **protons** and **electrons** and a variable number of **neutrons**.

Atomic number. The number of **protons** in the **nucleus** of an **atom**. This property specifically defines the **element**.

Atomic orbital. A theoretical description of the behavior of a single orbiting **electron** within the **electric field** of a **nucleus** and shielded by the other electrons in the **atom**. An electron in an orbital is defined by four **quantum numbers**: n, l, m_l, and m_s as given in the **electron configuration** for the atom.

Atomic radius. The distance from the middle of the **nucleus** of an **atom** to the outermost limit of the **electron shell**. On the periodic table, the magnitude:
- decreases from left to right
- increases from top to bottom in each group

Atomic weight. The average mass of an **atom** in a random sample of an **element** in nature. The average is influenced by the relative abundance of each **isotope** of the element.

Atria. The two smaller chambers of the **heart** that receive **blood** from the **lungs** (left atrium) or the **vena cava** (right atrium).

Atrioventricular node. A slender connection of specialized **cardiac muscle** that conducts **nerve impulses** from the **sinoatrial node** to the **ventricles**, causing them to contract.

Auditory canal. The tubular portion of the **external ear** that transmits **sound waves** to the **tympanic membrane**.

Autonomic nervous system. The network of involuntarily-controlled motor and **efferent neurons** and **ganglia** that make up the pathways of the **sympathetic** and **parasympathetic nervous systems**. These neurons innervate **cardiac muscle**, **smooth muscle**, and **glands**.

Autosomes. The 22 pairs of human **chromosomes**, not including the **sex chromosomes**.

Avogadro's law. States that equal volumes of different **ideal gases** at the same **temperature** and **pressure** contain equal numbers of **moles** or **molecules** (e.g., 22.4 L/mole of any ideal gas at **standard temperature and pressure**).

Avogadro's number. The number of particles in a **mole** of a particular substance:

$$6.02 \times 10^{23} \text{ particles/mole}$$

Axon. A single, long extension of the **neuron** that conducts **nerve impulses** away from the nerve **cell** body (e.g., toward a **muscle cell**, **gland**, or another neuron).

B

Bacillus. A cylindrically- or rod-shaped **bacterium**.

✔ Not all rod-shaped bacteria are of the genus *Bacillus*.

Bacteriophage. Any **virus** that specifically infects **bacteria** (see Appendix A, Figure 17).

Bacterium. A unicellular **microorganism** that lacks the distinct subcellular compartments and **organelles** found in **eukaryotes** (see Appendix A, Table 1).

Barr bodies. Inactivated excess X **chromosomes** in the body **cells** of females. Only one randomly determined X chromosome is active in each cell, thus preventing a redundancy of **gene** expression.

✔ This does not occur in males because male cells have only one X chromosome for which there is no homologue (the Y chromosome is not homologous to the X chromosome).

Base. Any substance that fits into one of the following three definitions.

1. According to the Brönsted-Lowry definition, a base is a chemical substance that can accept a **proton** from another substance.
2. The Brönsted-Lowry definition only slightly differs from Arrhenius's 1884 proposition that a base is an "**electrolyte** with an **anion** OH^-."
3. A Lewis base is a substance that can donate an **electron** pair.

Base pair. Two **nucleotides**, one on each of the two strands of a **deoxyribonucleic acid (DNA)** double-helix, that interact via **hydrogen bonding** between adjacent **nitrogenous bases**. The formation of base pairs reveals the complementarity of the two strands in the DNA helix because the specific pairings are invariable: guanine (G) always base pairs with cytosine (C) and thymine (T) always base pairs with adenine (A). The only time this rule appears to be broken is during **transcription**, when the nascent (new) **ribonucleic acid (RNA)** is transiently base-paired with its template DNA. Because RNA contains uracil (U) instead of thymine, there are uracil-adenine pairs in place of thymine-adenine pairs.

Basicity constant (K_b). The **equilibrium constant** for the reaction between a **weak base** and water. Generally expressed, it is:

$$B + H_2O \rightleftharpoons BH^+ + OH^-$$

$$K_b = \frac{[BH^+][OH^-]}{[B]}$$

Using carbonate as an example:

$$CO_3^{2-} + H_2O \rightleftharpoons HCO_3^- + OH^-$$

$$K_b = \frac{[HCO_3^-][OH^-]}{[CO_3^{2-}]} = 2.1 \times 10^{-4}$$

Compare to **acidity constant**

Basic salt. An **electrolyte** in which the **anion** is a **weak base**. A basic salt is always formed in the reaction between a **weak acid** and a **strong base**. Using Na_2S as an example:

Formation:

$$H_2S_{(aq)} \quad + \; 2\,NaOH \quad \leftrightharpoons Na_2S_{(aq)} \quad + \; 2H_2O$$

(weak acid) + (strong base) $\leftrightharpoons$ (basic salt)

Basic anion protonation:

$S^{2-} + 2H_2O \leftrightharpoons H_2S_{(aq)} + 2OH^-$ (hydroxide **ions** raise the **pH** of the **solution**)

✔ Due to the basicity of the anion, a solution containing a basic salt has a pH greater than 7.

Basilar membrane. A fibrous **tissue** in the **cochlea** that varies in stiffness along its length, causing each point on the membrane to vibrate in **resonance** with a unique **frequency** of **sound**. The **organ of Corti**, which lies directly on the membrane, generates a specific **nerve impulse** according to the point on the membrane that is resonating.

Battery. One or more **electrochemical cells** used to produce an **electromotive force** in a **circuit**.

Beat frequency. The detectable difference in **frequency** between two interfering **sound waves**:

$$f_B = |f_1 - f_2|$$

✔ Recall that $|a|$ = the absolute value (magnitude) of a.

Bernoulli's equation. A direct application of **Bernoulli's principle** and the law of **conservation of energy**. This equation relates the **pressure** to the **velocity** of a flowing **fluid**:

$$P + \rho gh + \tfrac{1}{2}\rho v^2 = \text{constant (at every point in the fluid), or}$$

$$P_1 + \tfrac{1}{2}\rho v_1^2 + \rho gh_1 = P_2 + \tfrac{1}{2}\rho v_2^2 + \rho gh_2$$

P = pressure of the fluid
ρ = **density** of the fluid
g = **acceleration** due to **gravity**
h = height of the fluid above a reference level
v = velocity of the fluid

Bernoulli's principle. Where the **velocity** of a **fluid** is high, the **pressure** is low, and vice versa. The principle is applied by using **Bernoulli's equation**.

Beta particle. An **electron** (negative) or, less commonly, a positron (positive, massless) that is released during beta decay of a radioactive **isotope**.

Bicuspid valve. The piece of valvular **tissue** that separates the left **atrium** from the left **ventricle**.

> *Also called* mitral valve

Bile. A mixture of bicarbonate, cholesterol, and **bile salts** that is secreted by the **liver**, stored in the **gallbladder**, and injected into the **duodenum** during meals.

Bile salts. Biologic detergent **molecules** that are the most important component of **bile**. Upon secretion into the **duodenum**, the salts emulsify ingested **fat** molecules and render them soluble in water, thus easing their absorption by the **intestinal villi**.

Binary fission. A method of asexual reproduction that produces two identical **haploid** daughter **cells** from one mother cell. This method of reproduction occurs in **bacteria** and some **fungi**.

Biochemical pathway. The organizational unit of **metabolism**.

Blastula. An early embryonic stage consisting of a spherical layer of **cells** called the trophoblast, an inner cell mass, and a central cavity called the blastocoel. This cluster of cells forms upon **cleavage** of the **zygote**.

> ✔ The cells of the blastula differ greatly from one another with regard to their size and amount of **cytoplasm**. The migration of some cells toward the center of the blastula is called **gastrulation**, which is a process that leads to the formation of the **gastrula**.

Blood. A circulating **fluid** that consists of blood **cells** (e.g., **erythrocytes**, **leukocytes**, **platelets**) and **blood plasma**. Blood composition is held constant by the regulatory activities of the **liver** and the **kidneys**. Blood transports nutrients and **gases** to and from the body **tissues**.

Blood plasma. The circulating **fluid** in which the components of the **blood**, such as water (90%), metabolites, wastes, **salts**, **ions**, **proteins**, and **hormones**, are suspended. It can be thought of as whole blood minus the blood **cells**.

> *See also* **serum**

Blood pressure. The **hydrostatic pressure** within the circulatory system that is often measured as arterial blood **pressure** at large **arteries** in the system (e.g., in the arm). It primarily depends on the strength of **cardiac muscle** contractions and the degree of **vasoconstriction** of the arteries. The maximum pressure reached during peak ventricular contraction is called systolic pressure; the minimum pressure just prior to ventricular contraction is called diastolic pressure. Arterial blood pressure is normally recorded as systolic/diastolic (e.g., 120/80).

Blood vessels. A network of tubes of varying diameters throughout the body that permit the circulation of **blood** from the **heart** to the **tissues**. Although the flow rate (i.e., the distance blood travels during a given time) is constant throughout the network, the **velocity** in individual vessels varies according to the diameters of the vessels.

> *See also* **artery, capillary, vein**

B lymphocyte (B cell). A type of **cell** that is derived from **bone marrow** and can be stimulated to differentiate in order to synthesize and secrete a specific **antibody** when confronted with an **antigen** that can be specifically bound by the cell's surface receptors. Every B cell is capable of secreting antibodies of only one specificity, and B cells of different lineages do not produce antibodies of similar specificities. This diversity increases the probability that at least one B cell is specific for any given antigen.

Bohr effect. A manifestation of the sensitivity and response of **hemoglobin** to **pH,** in which an increase in the gaseous carbon dioxide **partial pressure** increases the **concentration** of carbon dioxide dissolved in the **blood.** The resulting decrease in pH alters the shape of the hemoglobin **molecule** to facilitate oxygen unloading; therefore, oxygen is readily released at **tissues** where carbon dioxide concentration is high due to metabolic activity *(Figure 17).* The presence of lactic **acid** in active **muscle** has the same effect as carbon dioxide.

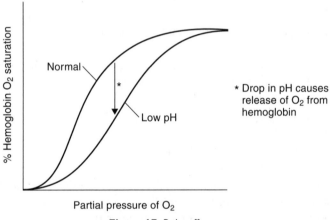

Figure 17. Bohr effect

✔ A drop in pH is due to the following reaction between water and carbon dioxide:

$$H_2O + CO_2 \leftrightharpoons H_2CO_3 \leftrightharpoons H^+ + HCO_3^-$$

Boiling point. The **temperature** at which the **vapor pressure** of a **liquid** equals the atmospheric **pressure**.

Boiling point elevation (ΔT_b). An increase in the **boiling point** of a **liquid** upon addition of a **solute.** This is a **colligative property** of **solutions.**

    ✔ The boiling point of a solution is always greater than that of the pure **solvent** when the solute is a **solid electrolyte.** However, when the solute has a lower boiling point than the solvent, as can occur with liquid solutes, the boiling point of the solution is not greater than that of the pure solvent.

    See also **freezing point depression**

Bond dissociation energy. The **enthalpy change** of a reaction in which a specific bond in a specific **molecule** is broken. This is a positive value because the reaction is always an **endothermic process.**

    Compare to **bond energy, enthalpy of formation**

Bond energy. The *average* value of the **energy** per **mole** required to break a particular bond in a variety of different **molecules** at 298 K.

> *Also called* bond enthalpy
> *Compare to* **bond dissociation energy**

Bone. A specialized form of structural **connective tissue** that consists of **collagen** fibers interspersed with mineral deposits. This composition allows bone to be rigid without being brittle.

> *See also* **compact bone, flat bone, long bone, spongy bone**
> *Compare to* **cartilage**

Bone marrow. A cellular substance contained within **spongy bone** that largely consists of fat cells and undifferentiated **stem cells**. It is within the bone cavities filled with marrow that **hemopoiesis** takes place.

Bowman's capsule. The first segment of the **nephron**, which wraps around the **glomerulus** and collects the filtrate that is driven out of the glomerular **capillaries**.

Boyle's law. The **pressure** (P) and volume (V) of a fixed quantity of an **ideal gas** are inversely related, given a constant **temperature**:

$$P \propto \frac{1}{V}, \text{ or}$$

$$PV = \text{constant}$$

> *See also* **Charles' law**

Brain. The part of the **central nervous system** that is located within the skull and is responsible for **muscle** control and coordination, sensory perception, speech, memory, and emotion (see Appendix A, Figure 9).

> *See also* **brain stem, cerebral cortex, cerebrum, hindbrain, hypothalamus, medulla oblongata, midbrain, pons**

Brain stem. The lowest portion of the **brain** that anatomically connects to the **spinal cord**. It includes the **medulla**, **pons**, and **midbrain**.

Bronchi. The pair of airways that lead from the **trachea** into each of the **lungs**, where they branch into several **bronchioles**.

Bronchioles. Airways that branch off from the **bronchi** and lead into alveolar sacs, which further subdivide into **alveoli**.

Brownian motion. The random movement of particles as evidence of the intrinsic motion and **kinetic energy** of **liquid** and **gas molecules**.

Buffer. A **solution** containing substantial amounts of a **weak acid** and its conjugate **weak base** that tends to maintain constant **pH** levels, within a certain range, upon addition of a **strong base** or **acid**. The equilibrium involved in the buffering action can be represented as:

$$HA^-_{(aq)} + H_2O \rightleftharpoons A^-_{(aq)} + H_3O^+$$

The addition of a strong acid to a solution would normally increase the **concentration** of H_3O^+, but in adherence to **Le Chatelier principle**, the presence of a basic salt permits an equilibrium shift toward the "left" that maintains the concentration of H_3O^+ reasonably constant. Likewise, upon addition of a strong base, the added OH^- neutralizes the H_3O^+, thus removing **protons** from the solution; an equilibrium shift toward the "right" compensates for this loss and maintains a constant pH. This effect can be readily observed in an acid-base **titration** because the titration curve remains fairly flat within the buffered range of the solution.

The **Henderson-Hasselbach equation** is used to determine the pH of a particular buffer that contains given concentrations of weak acid and weak base.

Efficient buffering has two requirements:

1. The number of **moles** of the weak acid and weak base must be relatively large compared to the number of moles of **base** or **acid** added to the buffer.
2. The conjugate base to weak acid **concentration** ratio must be approximately 1:1.

   ✔ In the human body, carbonic acid, phosphates, and **proteins** function as physiological buffers necessary for the maintenance of health.

Bulk modulus (B). A constant of proportionality that relates the hydraulic **pressure** (P), or **stress**, on an object to the magnitude of the change in volume (ΔV), or **strain**, of the object when it is submerged in a **fluid**:

$$P = B \left(\frac{\Delta V}{V} \right)$$

V = original volume of object

   ✔ The object is said to be under hydraulic **compression**.
   Compare to **shear modulus, Young's modulus**

Buoyant force (F_b). The buoyant **force** on a floating object is equal to the **weight** of the **fluid** displaced by the object, as given by:

$$F_b = V\rho g = mg$$

V = volume of fluid displaced by the object
ρ = **density** of the fluid
g = **acceleration** due to **gravity**
m = mass of the fluid of volume V

   ✔ Buoyant force is an application of **Archimedes' principle**.

C

Cahn-Ingold-Prelog nomenclature system. A set of sequence rules used in the description of molecular **configurations** to determine the "order of priority" of organic substituents.

1. If the **atoms** directly bound to the carbon are different, then the substituents are ordered according to the **atomic number** of those atoms. The highest atomic number confers the highest priority.
2. If two **isotopes** of the same **element** are present, then the isotope of higher mass receives the higher priority.
3. If two atoms directly bound to the carbon are identical, then the atomic numbers of the atoms at the first point of difference on each substituent chain are used to determine priority.
4. Atoms attached by double or triple bonds are given single-bond equivalencies. Each double-bonded atom is duplicated (or triplicated for triple bonds), as shown in *Figure 18.*

See also **absolute configuration**

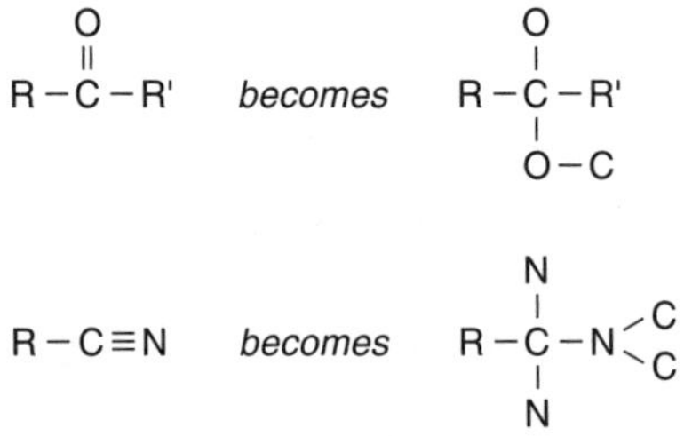

$$R - \underset{\underset{O}{\|}}{C} - R' \quad \textit{becomes} \quad R - \underset{\underset{O-C}{|}}{\overset{\overset{O}{|}}{C}} - R'$$

$$R - C \equiv N \quad \textit{becomes} \quad R - \underset{\underset{N}{|}}{\overset{\overset{N}{|}}{C}} - N \overset{C}{\underset{C}{}}$$

Figure 18. Cahn-Ingold-Prelog nomenclature system

Calcitonin. A **hormone** produced by the **thyroid gland** that lowers the **blood** calcium **concentration** by promoting the deposition of calcium in the **bones**.

Capacitance (C). The inherent property of a **capacitor** that determines its ability to store **energy**. The capacitance of a capacitor is a constant of proportionality in the relationship between the **potential difference** (V) across the plates and the charge (Q) on each plate:

$$C = \frac{Q}{V}$$

✔ The unit of capacitance, which is called a farad (F), is equal to one **coulomb** per **volt** (C/V).

Capacitor. A device that stores electric **potential energy** in an **electric field** between two **conductors** (plates) in close proximity, but not touching. If **voltage** is applied to the capacitor, the plates quickly acquire opposite charges, the magnitudes (Q) of which depend on the **po-**

tential difference (V) between the plates and the **capacitance** (C) of the capacitor *(Figure 19)*.

See also **dielectric**

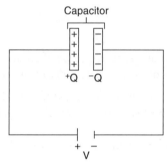

Figure 19. Capacitor

Capillary. The smallest type of **blood vessel** that connects the arterioles and venules and has thin membranes that permit the passive exchange of **gases** (i.e., oxygen and carbon dioxide) and **molecules** between the **blood** and **tissues**.

Capsid. The **protein** sheath that surrounds the **nucleic acid** core of a **virus**.

Capsule. An external, gelatinous (**polysaccharide**) layer that surrounds some forms of **bacteria** and can serve several functions, including food storage and prevention of **phagocytosis**. Its presence is often associated with heightened pathogenicity (i.e., ability to cause disease).

Carbanion. An **anion** containing a carbon **atom** bearing a negative charge.

Carbocation. A **cation** containing a positively-charged carbon **atom**. Although carbocations cannot be isolated, they are assumed to be common reaction intermediates in certain **addition**, **elimination**, and **substitution reactions**. The rate of a reaction involving a carbocation is dependent on the relative stability of the particular carbocation that is temporarily formed. The stability of the carbocation is increased by the distribution of the positive charge, a principle called the "inductive effect." A greater number of **alkyl groups** attached to the carbon atom increases the number of atoms that can share the positive charge and thus increases the stability of the carbocation *(Figure 20)*.

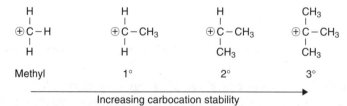

Figure 20. Relative carbocation stabilities

Carbohydrate. An organic **molecule** composed of a carbon chain or ring bound by oxygen and hydrogen and having the general formula [CH$_2$O]$_n$. Sugars (**monosaccharides**), **starch**, and **glycogen** are common examples of carbohydrates.

Carbonyl group. The functional group —C=O, which serves as the basis for the reactivity of both **aldehydes** and **ketones**. It consists of an sp^2-hybridized carbon **atom** joined to an oxygen atom by a **sigma bond** and a **pi bond**. The oxygen atom has two pairs of unshared **valence electrons**. The group is polar because the **electrons** in the double bond are drawn toward the **electronegative** oxygen.

Carboxylate anion. The **resonance**-stabilized conjugate base of a **carboxylic acid**, which is formed by the donation of an acidic **proton** to a suitable proton acceptor *(Figure 21)*. The stability of this **ion** accounts for the increased acidity of carboxylic acids relative to **alcohols** and **phenols**.

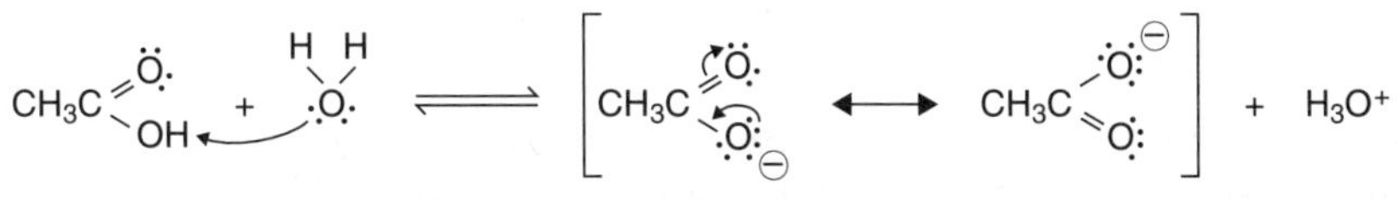

Ethanoic acid   Water   Resonance structures of the carboxylate anion

Figure 21. Carboxylate anion formation

Carboxyl group. The functional group —COOH, which contains a **carbonyl group** and a **hydroxyl group**. It is planar, polar (due to the **electronegative** oxygen **atoms**), and has two pairs of unshared **valence electrons** on each oxygen atom.

See also **carboxylate anion, carboxylic acids**

Carboxylic acids. Organic **molecules** that characteristically contain **carboxyl groups** and serve as weak, organic **acids** with **pK$_a$** values of approximately 5 [e.g., ethanoic acid *(Figure 22)*]. Carboxylic acids are characterized by polarity of the carboxyl group; solubility in water and organic **solvents** (lower **molecular weight** acids only); increased acidity due to **resonance** stability of the **carboxylate anion**; strong **hydrogen bonding** between acid molecules; relatively high **melting point** and **boiling point**; and varied acidity due to substituents that have inductive effects that can decrease or increase the acidity.

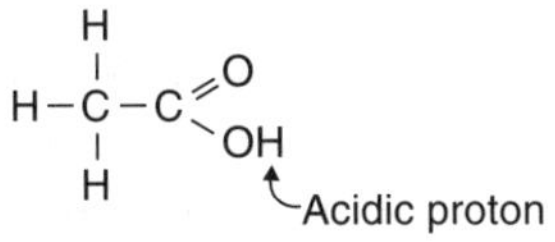

Figure 22. Acetic acid

Cardiac muscle. A **syncytium** of striated, branched **muscle fibers** composed of uninucleated **muscle cells** joined to one another by transmembrane structures called **intercalated discs** *(Figure 23)*. Although the cardiac muscle is highly innervated by **neurons** of the **autonomic nervous system**, depolarization is only initiated at specific nodes (e.g., **sinoatrial node**) from which the **action potentials** spread to other **cells** via **gap junctions**. This synchronization of cell contractions produces the pumping action that consistently propels **blood** toward the body **tissues**.

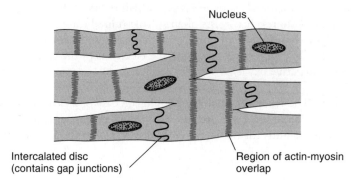

Figure 23. Cardiac muscle

Cartilage. A special type of **connective tissue** that contains **collagen** and is found at positions of mechanical **stress** (e.g., **bone** joints). Cartilage is firm, but flexible enough to withstand large amounts of **tension**.

Catabolism. The general term for any biochemical action that results in the breakdown of complex **molecules** into simpler molecules.

Catalyst. A substance that lowers the **activation energy** of a chemical reaction, thus increasing the rate of reaction. The catalyst is not consumed during the reaction; it does not affect the **equilibrium constant**.

   See also **enzyme**

Cathode. The **electrode** where **reduction** occurs. It has a positive charge in **electrochemical cells** and a negative charge in **electrolytic cells**.

   Compare to **anode**

Cation. An **ion** with a positive charge.

Cell. (1) A biological cell is the smallest living structural unit of any organism. (2) An **electrochemical cell** or **electrolytic cell**.

Cell-mediated immune response. The selective **differentiation** and activation of a subset of **cytotoxic T lymphocytes** that can specifically recognize and lyse body **cells** that are infected with an intracellular parasite, are foreign to the host, or display cell-surface **proteins** indicative of malignancy (i.e., a cancerous cell). The response is dependent on the presence of particular **cytokines** secreted primarily by **helper T cells**.

   Compare to **humoral immune response**

Cell membrane. See **plasma membrane**

Cell potential. See **electromotive force**

Cellular respiration. A general term for the series of **energy**-yielding oxidation-reduction reactions that occur during **glycolysis** and the **Krebs cycle**. The **cell** extracts **electrons** from the chemical bonds of fuel **molecules** (e.g., **glucose**) and can use these electrons to drive **proton** pumps to generate **adenosine triphosphate (ATP)** by a process known as **oxidative phosphorylation**. ATP can also be synthesized by *directly* harnessing the energy of fuel molecules in a process known as substrate-level phosphorylation.

See also **electron transport chain, fermentation**

Cell voltage. See **electromotive force**

Cell wall. A rigid, external layer that surrounds plant **cells**, most **bacteria**, and various other single-celled organisms.

Center of mass. The single point in a physical body whose motion can always be described as similar to that of a particle. If the **force** of **gravity** is constant throughout the body (as it would be on Earth), then the center of mass is the same as the center of gravity.

Central nervous system. The body system composed of the **brain** and **spinal cord**, which are the sites of the body's information processing capabilities.

Compare to **peripheral nervous system**

Centriole. A eukaryotic, cytoplasmic structure from which the **spindle apparatus** originates during animal cell **mitosis** and **meiosis**. During **cell** division, there is a centriole at each pole of the cell.

Centromere. A specific **deoxyribonucleic acid** sequence within each **chromosome** that serves as the binding point between sister **chromatids**. The centromere is the site at which the **kinetochore** is associated with the paired chromatids.

Cerebellum. The portion of the **hindbrain** that coordinates muscular movements by integrating information about changes in the position and motion of the body. It is located above the **medulla** and behind the **forebrain**.

Cerebral cortex. The outer layer of the **cerebrum** where much of the perception, thinking, and reasoning activities are localized; it is also where memories are stored.

Cerebrum. The dominant portion of the **brain**. It comprises two joined hemispheres that serve as the primary centers of sensory input and motor response coordination. It is also the origin of most conscious thought processes.

Cervix. A muscular sphincter that defines the opening to the **uterus**.

Charles' law. At constant **pressure**, the **temperature** (T) and volume (V) of an **ideal gas** are directly proportional to one another:

$$T \propto V$$

Also called Gay-Lussac's law
See also **Boyle's law**

Chemiosmosis. A general term referring to the coupling of chemical reactions ("chemi") with transport processes ("osmosis"). Most commonly, it is the generation of a **protonmotive force** as a result of the mitochondrial **electron transport chain**, which together compose the **adenosine triphosphate**-producing process called **oxidative phosphorylation**.

Chiasma. The region of contact between **homologous chromosomes** where **crossing-over** occurred during **synapsis**.

Chief cell. A type of **exocrine gland cell** in the **stomach mucosa** that secretes pepsinogen, which is a precursor **protein** that is converted into **pepsin** upon contact with the hydrochloric acid in the stomach.

Chiral carbon atom. See **chiral center**

Chiral center. An sp^3-hybridized carbon **atom** with four different attached groups.

> ✔ The carbon atom can be referred to as a "chiral carbon." However, it is technically the **molecule**, not just the atom itself, that exhibits **chirality**.

Chirality. The property of nonsuperimposability of a **molecule** upon its mirror image. A chiral molecule does not have a plane of symmetry.

> *See also* **absolute configuration**

Cholecystokinin. A **hormone** secreted by the **duodenum** when food enters the **small intestine**. It stimulates the **gallbladder** to release **bile** and induces the **pancreas** to release other digestive **enzymes**.

Chordate. An animal that belongs to the phylum Chordata. Chordates are characterized by single, hollow **nerve** cords and, at some point in their development, a dorsal **notochord** and pharyngeal slits. They include animals such as fish, amphibians, reptiles, birds, and mammals.

Chorion. Within the **uterus**, it is the outermost membrane that surrounds the **embryo** and interacts with the **endometrium** to form the **placenta**.

> *See also* **amnion**

Choroid. The middle layer of the eye, located between the **retina** and the **sclera**, which contains the **blood vessels** that provide nutritive supplies to the **rods** and **cones** of the retina. This layer also contains the black **pigment**, melanin, that prevents light from reflecting or scattering in the eyeball.

Chromatid. One of the two daughter copies of a duplicated **chromosome**, which remains paired with its sister via an attachment at a single **centromere** *(Figure 24)*. The sister chromatids separate at **anaphase** of **mitosis** or anaphase II of **meiosis**.

Chromatin. A complex cellular structure consisting of a **deoxyribonucleic acid** double helix and **protein**. It is contained in the **nucleus** and is the material of which eukaryotic **chromosomes** are composed.

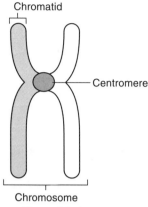

Figure 24. Chromatid

Chromatography. A technique used to separate compounds according to their differential adsorption (binding) to a **liquid** or **solid**. There are a variety of chromatographic methods, most of which involve the flowing of a mixture in a **solvent** or a carrier **gas** (mobile phase) through a column of adsorbent material (stationary phase). The relative affinities that different compounds have for the mobile phase and the stationary phase permit the separation of the components of the mixture.

> ✔ A detailed description of these techniques is beyond the scope of this book. However, you should be familiar with the method and application of gas-liquid chromatography and thin-layer chromatography.

Chromosome. A highly condensed (except during replication), coiled **molecule** that is responsible for physically transmitting hereditary information from parent to offspring. In **bacteria**, each chromosome is a single, circular strand of **deoxyribonucleic acid**. In eukaryotic **cells**, each chromosome is a single, linear strand of **chromatin**.

Cilia. Numerous, short, hair-like external extensions of the **plasma membrane**. In humans, **cells** on the surface of the **trachea** have cilia composed of a coordinated set of **microtubules** that move mucus and debris from airways. Cilia can also be a means of locomotion in some protozoa.

Ciliary action. The coordinated movement of **cilia** in the **trachea**, which serves to clean the inspired air of large particles before it moves into the **lungs**.

Ciliary muscle. A **muscle** in the eye that alters the shape of the **lens** during **accommodation** and is controlled almost entirely by parasympathetic **nerve** signals. For example, parasympathetic stimulation causes the muscles to contract, thus relaxing the **tension** on the lens and allowing it to become more spherical. This results in an increased refractive **power** (i.e., increased ability to focus on close objects).

Circuit. A continuous (closed) electrical **conduction** pathway formed by a wire connected to both terminals of a **battery** and through which a **current** can flow *(Figure 25)*.

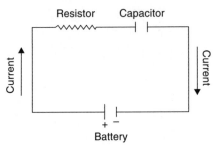

Figure 25. Circuit components

***Cis-trans* isomers.** See **geometric isomers**

Citric acid cycle. See **Krebs cycle**

Cleavage. A general term commonly used to describe the rapid division of the vertebrate **zygote**, which produces a hollow ball of **cells** called the **blastula**.

Cline. A gradual genetic variation in a species due to environmental changes in the habitat.

Clitoris. A sensitive knob of **tissue** located between the minor folds of the **labia**; it is analogous to the glans penis in the male.

Cocci. A term used to describe a **bacterium** that is spherical or ovoid in shape.

Cochlea. The spiral-shaped tubular canal of the **inner ear** that is filled with **fluid** and contains most of the hearing **organs**.

> ✔ The term cochlea is basically synonymous with the inner ear.

> *See also* **basilar membrane, organ of Corti**

Codominance. A genetic relationship between two different **alleles** of a particular **gene** that are simultaneously expressed. In the **heterozygote**, each codominant allele contributes a phenotypic feature that is distinguishable (e.g., a person with AB **blood** type has **erythrocytes** expressing both A and B types of surface **antigen**).

> *See also* **heterozygous**
> *Compare to* **incomplete dominance**

Codon. A sequence of three adjacent **nucleotides** (triplet code) on **messenger ribonucleic acid** that specifies a particular **amino acid** or **polypeptide** chain termination signal *(Figure 26)*.

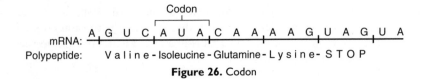

Figure 26. Codon

Coenzyme. A nonprotein **molecule** associated with an **enzyme**; a **cofactor** that transiently and weakly binds to **protein** (compared to **prosthetic groups**, which remain tightly bound to the enzyme). It often acts as an **electron** donor or acceptor and can be composed of substances such as **vitamins** and metal **ions**. Some examples of coenzymes are NAD$^+$ and coenzyme A.

Cofactor. A compound that is not an **amino acid**, yet is a crucial component of a functional complex **enzyme**. Cofactors can be **coenzymes** or **prosthetic groups**.

> ✔ Not all enzymes require an association with a cofactor.

Cohesion. Attractive **forces** among **molecules** of the same substance.

> *Compare to* **adhesion**

Collagen. A strong, fibrous **protein** that is almost always secreted by **fibroblasts**. It is the primary component of most **connective tissue** (e.g., **cartilage**, **tendon**, **ligament**, **bone**) and is the most abundant protein in the bodies of **vertebrates**.

Collecting duct. This tube arises from the **collecting tubules** of several **nephrons** and is the final site of **urine** processing. Its unique permeability to **urea** allows the **diffusion** of urea out of the duct and into the surrounding **tissue**, where its **concentration** is relatively low due to the lack of urea reabsorption in the earlier portions of the nephron. The resulting increase in the concentration of urea in the **kidney** tissue, coupled with the increased **ion** concentration due to ion reabsorption in earlier portions of the nephron, causes water to diffuse by **osmosis** out of the collecting duct, thus resulting in a more concentrated urine. **Antidiuretic hormone** increases the duct's permeability to water, leading to increased reabsorption of water and the retention of body **fluid**.

Collecting tubule. The portion of the **nephron** that follows from the **distal convoluted tubule**. It actively reabsorbs sodium **ions** while secreting potassium ions into the tubular **fluid** and is almost completely impermeable to **urea**. Its ability to secrete hydrogen ions permits the acid-base regulation of the body fluids. Unlike the ascending limb of the **loop of Henle** and the distal convoluted tubule, the collecting tubule is conducive to the **diffusion** of water into the interstitium, which is **hyperosmotic** compared to the tubular fluid. The permeability of the collecting tubule to water is subject to the effects of two major **hormones**: **aldosterone** (indirectly increases the rate of water reabsorption by upregulating sodium reabsorption) and **antidiuretic hormone** (directly increases the permeability of the membrane to water).

> ✔ Reabsorption refers to the movement of substances from the tubular fluid (future **urine**) back into the interstitial **tissue** of the **kidney**. Secretion is the opposite movement of substances from the kidney interstitium into the tubular fluid.

> ✔ At the point when the collecting tubule is conducive to the diffusion of water into the interstitium, the interstitium is hyperosmotic (compared to the tubular fluid) because the reabsorption of sodium by the distal convoluted tubule and the ascending limb of the loop of Henle occurs in the absence of water permeability and, therefore, builds up high **concentrations** of **solute** in the interstitial tissue. In essence, the collecting tubule "undilutes" the tubular fluid.

Colligative properties. Properties of a substance that are affected by the number of particles present, not by the nature of the particles themselves.

> *Compare to* **intensive properties**

Colon. The large intestine; this portion of the gastrointestinal tract acts as a refuse dump where relatively little absorption of **fluid** takes place.

Combustion. The rapid reaction of a compound with molecular oxygen, which is accompanied by the release of light and **heat**. All combustion reactions are **exothermic**. Using hydrocarbon combustion as an example:

$$CH_4 + 2O_2 \leftrightharpoons CO_2 + 2H_2O$$

Common ion effect. A shift in the **solubility** equilibrium of an insoluble compound due to the **Le Chatelier principle**. The solubility of an insoluble **electrolyte** is significantly decreased in the presence of a soluble electrolyte that has an **ion** in common with the insoluble electrolyte. Despite the changes in the solubility, the **solubility product (K_{sp})** is not affected as long as the **temperature** remains constant. Using the dissociation of lead sulphate as an example:

$$PbSO_{4(s)} \rightleftharpoons Pb^{2+}_{(aq)} + SO^{2-}_{4(aq)}$$

When $[Pb^{2+}]$ is increased by adding $Pb(NO_3)$ to the **solution**, the $[SO_4^{2-}]$ must decrease so that the solubility product remains constant:

$$K_{sp}(PbSO_4) = [Pb^{2+}][SO_4^{2-}] = 1.8 \times 10^{-8} \text{ M}^2$$

    ✔ Referring to an electrolyte as insoluble may seem like a paradox, but it is just a designation that is used to indicate a greatly reduced ability to dissolve in comparison to so-called soluble electrolytes.

Compact bone. Dense, calcified layers of **connective tissue** found on the periphery of the **long bones**. It surrounds the inner **spongy bone** tissue, has dense **collagen** fibrils, and forms the strongest component of **bone**.

Complement. A cascade (i.e., functional series) of **blood**-bound **proteins** that are attracted to **cells** tagged by **antibodies** or expressing unique complement-binding surface components. These proteins aid in the destruction of foreign or infected cells by causing their **lysis** during an **immune response**.

Compression. A **stress** (**force** per unit area) in which forces acting inward on a **solid** are directed toward one another. Any object supporting the **weight** of another, such as the leg of a chair, is subject to compression.

    Also called compressive stress
    Compare to **tension**

Concave mirror. A concave (i.e., center of the sphere bulges away from the viewer) reflecting surface. For an object infinitely far away, a concave mirror causes the convergence of parallel incident light, which forms an image at the **focal point** *(Figure 27)*. The **mirror equation** relates object and image distances to the **focal length** (f), which is the distance between the focal point and the mirror. By convention, the focal length and the radius of curvature (r) of a concave mirror are positive.

    ✔ If the object is within the focal length, the image is **virtual**, upright, and magnified. If the object is beyond the focal point, the image is **real** and inverted. The magnification depends on placement relative to the center of curvature (C).

    Compare to **convex mirror**

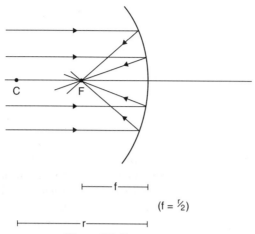

(f = $\frac{r}{2}$)

Figure 27. Concave mirror

Concentration. The quantity of a **solute** in a **solvent**, which is usually stated in terms of **molarity**, **molality**, or **mole fraction**.

Concentration cell. An electrochemical apparatus (**galvanic cell**) that produces a **current** and **voltage** as the result of a difference in the **concentrations** of the same substance at the **anode** and **cathode**.

Condensation. (1) The **exothermic** conversion of a **gas** to its **liquid** state. (2) When referring to a **wave**, it is the area where a **longitudinal wave** is compressed or, for a **sound** wave, where there is a high **density** of air **molecules**. A condensation is analagous to a crest of a **transverse wave**.

Condensation reaction. A chemical reaction in which two or more **molecules** combine to form a larger molecule, and a small molecule (usually water) is lost. Examples of condensation reactions include **aldol condensation** and **polymerization** reactions (e.g., formation of **polysaccharides**, **polypeptides**).

Compare to **dehydration**

Conduction. (1) The transfer of **heat energy** by molecular collisions, which occurs when there is a difference in **temperature** between two adjacent media. (2) The flow of **electrons** that occurs when two **conductors** touch.

Compare to **convection, induction, radiation**

Conductor. A material that readily carries and transmits electric charge (usually a metal).

Compare to **insulator**

Cone. A type of **photoreceptor** in the **retina** that is sensitive to bright light and color. The cones are concentrated at the **fovea**. Each cone contains blue-sensitive, red-sensitive, or green- sensitive photochemicals (**pigments**); color detection is based on the unique combination of cones that are stimulated.

Compare to **rod**

Configuration. The spatial sequence of substituents (**atoms** or functional groups) attached to a **chiral center**, surrounding a double bond, or within a cyclic compound where there is structural rigidity. Interconversion between different configurations requires breakage of bonds. The maximum number of different configurations of a compound with n **chiral carbon atoms** is equal to 2^n; however, if **meso compounds** are possible, the compound will have less than 2^n configurations.

> *See also* **absolute configuration, relative configuration**
> *Compare to* **conformation**

Conformation. The spatial arrangement of a **molecule** that results from a rotation about a single carbon-carbon bond. Interconversion between different conformations usually occurs at room **temperature**; thus, isolation of a particular conformation is difficult. Common conformations can be illustrated using *Newman projections*, which are diagrams that involve a view of the molecule directly along a carbon-carbon axis. Common conformations include:

1. staggered conformation, in which there is a 60° angle between the C-H bonds on adjacent carbon **atoms** *(Figure 28)*

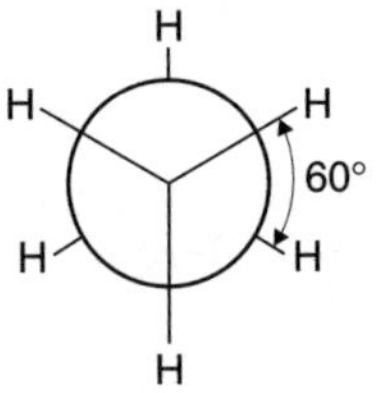

Figure 28. Staggered conformation of ethane

2. eclipsed conformation, in which there is a 0° (or 120°) angle between C-H bonds on adjacent carbon atoms *(Figure 29)*

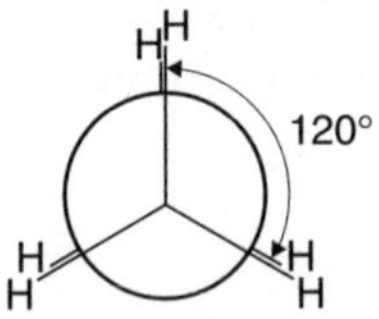

Figure 29. Eclipsed conformation of ethane

3. anti conformation, which is a staggered conformation of butane in which the **methyl groups** are farthest apart from one another *(Figure 30)*

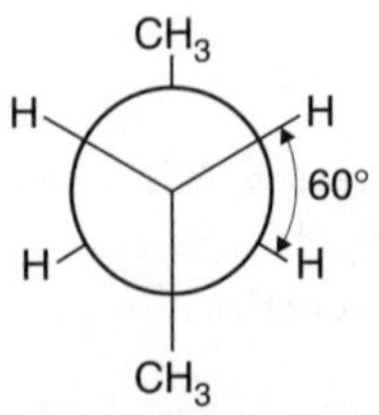

Figure 30. Anti conformation of butane

4. gauche conformation, which is a staggered conformation of butane in which the methyl groups are adjacent to one another *(Figure 31)*

    Compare to **configuration**

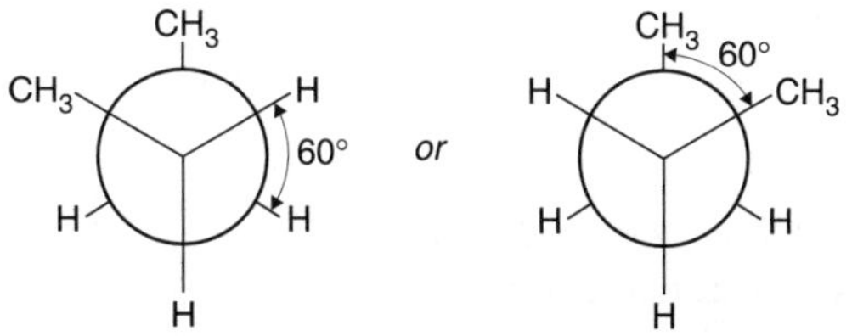

Figure 31. Gauche conformation of butane

Conjugate acid-base pair. An **acid** and a **base** whose structures differ only by a single **proton**. They are related by the general equation: base + H^+ = acid. The pair is always comprised of a **strong base** and a **weak**(er) **acid**, or vice versa.

Conjugation. The temporary pairing of "male" and "female" forms of unicellular organisms during which an exchange of genetic material occurs. In **bacteria**, this transfer is mediated by intercellular structures called pili.

   Compare to **transduction, transformation**

Conjunctiva. A thin, mucus-secreting **epithelium** that covers the **cornea** and exposed parts of the **sclera** of the eye. It is transparent where it covers the cornea.

Connective tissue. A general class of **tissues** composed of **cells** derived from the **mesoderm** which characteristically embed themselves in nonliving, **extracellular matrices (ECM)** and provide defensive, structural, or storage functions. Depending on the cell-to-ECM ratio, structural connective tissue can be classified as dense (e.g., **tendon**) or loose (e.g., the layer of **dermis** closest to the **epidermis**). Examples of connective tissues include **bone, cartilage**, tendons, **ligaments**, and immune cells (in a matrix of **blood plasma**).

Conservation of energy. See **first law of thermodynamics**

Conservation of mass. A basic principle of chemistry that affirms that the number of **moles** of all **atoms** of an **element** in a reaction remains the same before and after the reaction occurs.

Constitutional isomers. Isomers that differ only in the order and arrangement of **atoms** and bonds. For example, C_4H_{10} has two constitutional isomers *(Figure 32)*.

   Also called structural isomers
   Compare to **geometric isomers, stereoisomers**

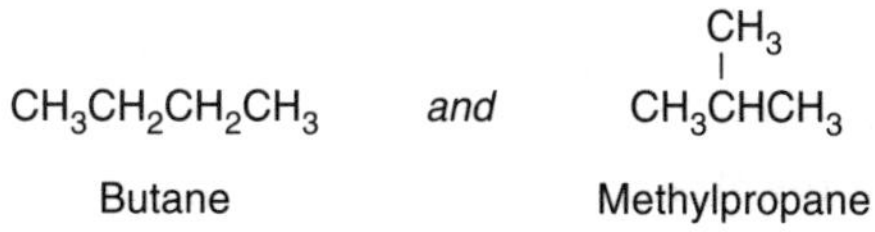

Figure 32. Constitutional isomers

Constructive interference. The phenomenon by which **waves** add together (**superposition**) to produce a larger resultant wave than either of the original waves. Maximum summation occurs when the **phase difference** (ϕ) is equal to the **wavelength** (2π).

Compare to **destructive interference**

Continuity equation. A formula that represents the volume rate of flow of a **fluid**:

$$\text{constant} = A_1 v_1 = A_2 v_2$$

A = the area through which the fluid passes
v = the **velocity** of flow at that point

Therefore, where the cross-sectional area is large, the velocity is small, and vice versa.

Convection. The transfer of **heat** by the actual movement of **molecules** over relatively large distances. For example, heat **energy** from **cell** processes is released from the surface of the skin into the environment by convection, **evaporation**, and **radiation**.

Compare to **conduction**

Converging lens. Any thin **lens** that is wider at the middle than at its ends and refracts parallel light rays causing their convergence at a **focal point** (F) *[Figure 33]*. The **focal length** (f) is always positive for a converging lens. An object placed at a distance from the lens that is farther than the focal point produces a **real image**; an object placed within the focal length results in a **virtual image**.

Also called positive lens
Compare to **diverging lens**

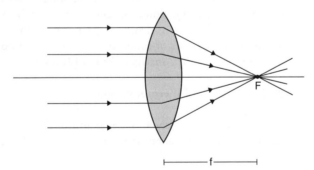

Figure 33. Converging lens

Convex mirror. A convex (i.e., the center of the sphere bulges toward the viewer) reflecting surface. For an object infinitely far away, a convex mirror causes the divergence of parallel incident light; however, the reflected rays appear to originate at the **focal point** (F) at a distance, the **focal length** (f), behind the mirror *(Figure 34)*. The **mirror equation** relates the object (o) and image (i) distances to the focal length. By convention, the focal length and the radius of curvature (r) of a convex mirror are negative. The image formed is always **virtual**, upright, and smaller than the object.

Compare to **concave mirror**

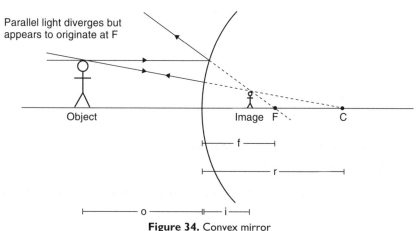

Parallel light diverges but
appears to originate at F

Object   Image F   C

f

r

o   i

Figure 34. Convex mirror

Cornea. The clear portion of the outer membrane of the eye. It is continuous with the **sclera** and is important for the **refraction** (i.e., focusing) of light rays.

Corona radiata. The collection of **cells** surrounding the **ovum**. These cells are dissolved by the contents of the **acrosome** upon penetration by a **sperm** cell.

Coronary circulation. The network of **blood vessels** that supply **blood** to the **cardiac muscle**.

Corpus luteum. The remains of the ruptured **follicle** in the **ovary** after **ovulation** occurs; it continues to secrete **estrogen** and **progesterone** to prepare the **uterus** for **fertilization**.

Corticosteroids. A class of **hormones** secreted by the **adrenal cortex** that are all synthesized from cholesterol, yet have different functions. The two most important examples are **aldosterone** and cortisol, the latter of which has a wide variety of effects including **metabolism**, immunity, and anti-inflammatory mechanisms.

Coulomb (C). The most common unit of electric charge. It is defined as 1 A · s.

See also **ampere**

Coulomb's law. Electric charges at rest exert attractive or repulsive **forces** upon one another that are inversely proportional to the square of the **distance** between the charges. The magnitude of the force that one resting charge exerts on another is described in the following equation:

$$F = \frac{k(Q_1 Q_2)}{r^2}$$

Q_1 and Q_2 = the magnitudes of the two charges (in **coulombs**)
k = 8.988 × 10⁹ N · m²/C² ≅ 9.0 × 10⁹ N · m²/C²
r = the distance between the two charges

✔ The direction of the force is along the "line" that joins the two charges.

✔ When several charges are present, the net force on any one of them is the **vector** sum of all the forces of the surrounding charges (e.g., $F_{net} = F_1 + F_2 + \ldots$).

Covalent bond. A chemical bond formed by the sharing of one or more pairs of **electrons** between two **atoms** (prevalent in nonmetallic compounds). The sharing can be unequal due to differing **electronegativities** of the two atoms; in such cases, the bond is considered to be polar covalent.

Cranial nerves. The twelve peripheral **nerves** arising from the **brain**, which can have sensory, motor, or mixed functions. Several of the cranial nerves are parasympathetic fibers.

Creatinine. A waste product of **muscle metabolism** that is continuously released into the **blood plasma** and is excreted into the **urine**.

Cristae. The folds of the inner membranes of **mitochondria** where **oxidative phosphorylation** occurs.

Critical angle (Θ_c). The particular angle of incidence (Θ_i) that causes an angle of **refraction** (Θ_r) of 90° when light enters a medium for which the **index of refraction** (n) is less than that of the medium where the light originated *(Figure 35A)*. The refracted ray runs along the border between the two media. Refraction occurs when $\Theta_i < \Theta_c$ (Figure 35B), whereas **total internal reflection** occurs when $\Theta_i > \Theta_c$ (Figure 35C).

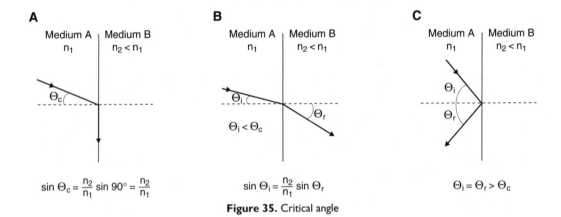

Figure 35. Critical angle

Crossing-over. The exchange of corresponding genetic sequences between **homologous chromosomes** during **prophase** I of **meiosis**; it occurs by a process of chromosomal **recombination**.

Current, electrical. A stream of moving charges caused by a **potential difference** between two points. The amount of positive charge that passes a given point within a certain time is given by the equation:

$$i = \frac{q}{t}$$

i = current (in **amperes**)
q = charge (in **coulombs**)
t = time (in seconds)

✔ When discussing the direction of the current, it is by convention that we refer to the flow of positive charges. Therefore, the conventional current (i.e., the flow of positive charges from the positive terminal to the negative terminal of a **battery**) is in the opposite direction of the **electron** flow.

Cyanide. A potent chemical inhibitor of the **electron transport chain**.

Cytochrome. An iron-containing **protein** compound that transfers **electrons** in an **electron transport chain** during **cell metabolism**.

Cytokine. A general term for a soluble chemical messenger, commonly a small glycoprotein, which facilitates communication between the body's **cells**. Cytokines, which include **interferons**, the interleukins (cytokines that act on or are secreted by **leukocytes**), and some chemotactic factors (chemical attractants), are commonly referred to when describing the regulation of an **immune response**. These chemical mediators can be partially distinguished from other **hormones** by pleiotropism (a single cytokine can have numerous target cells); redundancy (different cytokines have similar effects); and the brief, self-limiting nature of their effects.

Cytokinesis. The division of a **cell**'s **cytoplasm** that follows **mitosis**.

Cytoplasm. The entire interior region of a **cell**, excluding the **nucleus**. It consists of two components: the **cytosol** and cell **organelles** other than the nucleus.

Cytosol. A semifluid matrix within the **cell** that surrounds all cell **organelles**.

Cytoskeleton. A complex cytoplasmic network of **microfilaments**, **intermediate filaments**, and **microtubules**. It contributes to the maintenance of **cell** structure, shape, and intracellular organization. Other functions of the cytoskeletal **proteins** involve cell motility, cell division (e.g., the **spindle apparatus**), and intercellular communication.

Cytotoxic T lymphocyte. A type of circulating **leukocyte** derived from **bone marrow** that will, upon stimulation by **helper T cells**, directly lyse body **cells** infected by a pathogen (e.g., **virus**).

See also **cell-mediated immune response**

D

Dalton's law. The total **pressure** of a mixture of any number of **ideal gases** is equal to the sum of the **partial pressures** of the **gases** in the mixture. The equation that permits calculation of the total pressure is:

$$P_{total} = \Sigma P_i = n_{total} \left(\frac{RT}{V} \right)$$

ΣP_i = the sum of the partial pressures
n_{total} = the total number of **moles** of gas
R = universal gas constant = 8.2×10^{-2} L · atm/mo · K
T = the **temperature** in degrees Kelvin
V = the total volume occupied by the mixture of gases

The law can also be expressed in terms of the **mole fraction** of one component:

$$P_{total} = \frac{P_i}{X_{i\ (gas)}}$$

P_i = partial pressure
$X_{i\ (gas)}$ = mole fraction

Decarboxylation. The loss of CO_2 in a chemical reaction. For example, β-keto acids (**carboxylic acids** with β-**carbonyl groups**) undergo decarboxylation when heated *(Figure 36)*.

✔ Remember that a substituent at the "β" position of a carboxylic acid is attached to the carbon **atom** that is "two away" from the **carboxyl group** (—COOH).

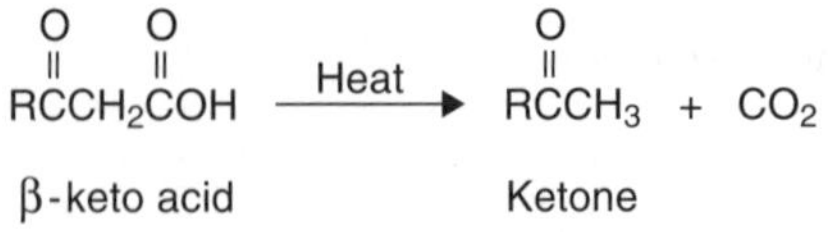

Figure 36. Decarboxylation

Dehydration. An **elimination reaction** in which there is a loss of water. The reaction is usually promoted by **heat** and the presence of a **strong acid. Alcohols** are common participants of dehydration reactions *(Figure 37)*.

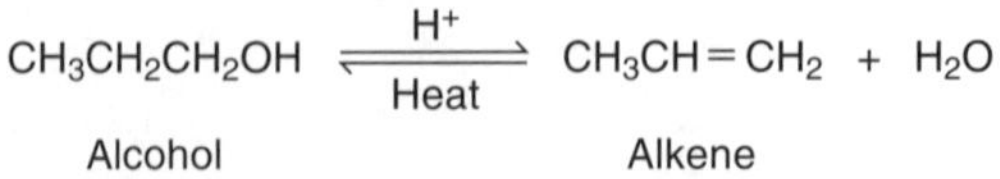

Figure 37. Dehydration of an alcohol

Dehydrogenation. An **elimination reaction** in which there is a loss of hydrogen from a **hydrocarbon** or alcohol. The reaction is usually catalyzed by **heat**.

Denaturation. An alteration of the normal **configuration** of a **protein** that often results in its loss of function and its **precipitation** from **solution**. The change can be caused by a non-physiologic **pH**, excessive **heat**, or changes in the ionic strength of the protein solution.

Dendrite. A cytoplasmic extension from a **nerve** cell body that conducts **impulses** or **action potentials** toward the **cell** body. Dendrites are typically short and branched. A single nerve cell body often contains numerous dendrites, as opposed to a singular **axon**.

Density. (1) The density of a **gas** or **solid** is the mass per unit volume of matter. (2) The density of a **solution** is the mass of total solution per unit volume of the total solution.

Deoxyribonucleic acid (DNA). An unbranched **polymer** consisting of four different types of subunits (**nucleotides**), which are linked to one another by covalent **phosphodiester bonds**. DNA contains the genetic information ("blueprints") in all organisms. It is most commonly found as a double-stranded, helical **molecule**. The two strands are complementary and anti-parallel in relation to one another and are associated by **hydrogen bonding** between complementary **base pairs** *(Figure 38)*. Local unwinding of the helix allows either **replication** of the duplex or **transcription** of **messenger ribonucleic acid** copies of **genes**.

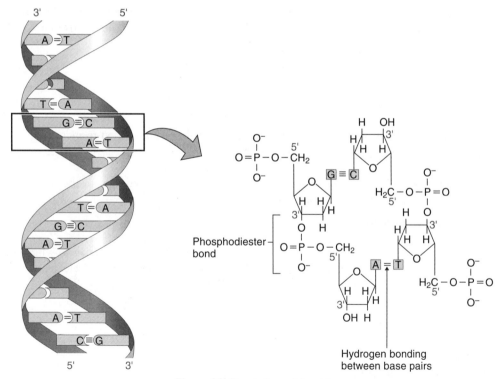

Figure 38. Deoxyribonucleic acid

Deoxyribonucleic acid polymerase. The **enzyme** that synthesizes a **deoxyribonucleic acid (DNA)** strand in a 5′ to 3′ direction by catalyzing the addition of **nucleotides** to the 3′ end of the DNA **polymer**. The specific nucleotide sequence of the nascent strand is complementary to that of the DNA template strand.

See also **base pair, deoxyribonucleic acid**

Depolarization. A shift in the **membrane potential** to a less negative value. If the membrane is depolarized beyond a threshold level, local voltage-gated sodium channels open, allowing Na^+ to flow into the **cell**. In **neurons** and **muscle cells**, this local disruption initiates a small **current** that influences neighboring sodium channels to open, thus allowing an **action potential** to be propagated. This can result in a reversal of the membrane potential to a positive value (approximately $+50$ mV), at which point the sodium channels close and potassium channels open. The membrane then reverts back to its **resting potential**.

Dermis. The layer of the skin that is internal to the **epidermis**. It is composed of a layer of loose **connective tissue**, which is directly adjacent to the **epithelium**. Below the loose connective tissue is a layer of dense connective tissue. The dermis contains accessory structures including **blood vessels**, sensory **nerve** endings, hair **follicles**, sweat **glands**, sebaceous glands, **fibroblasts**, and **macrophages**.

Desmosome. A type of anchoring **cell** junction that is essentially a small, button-like point of contact and adhesion between two adjacent cells. The junction provides a point of connection between the **cytoskeletons** of the adjacent cells.

Destructive interference. The interaction of two or more **waves (superposition)** that results in a wave that is smaller than any of the original waves. The maximum reduction in **amplitude** takes place when the waves are completely out of phase, i.e., the **phase difference** (Φ) is equal to an odd multiple of π:

$$\Phi = (n + \tfrac{1}{2})2\pi$$

$n = 0, 1, 2, \ldots$
$2\pi =$ one **wavelength**

Determination. The process by which **differentiating cells** are committed to increasingly specific fates as the development of an organism proceeds.

Dextrorotatory. Refers to an **enantiomer** that rotates plane-polarized light to the right. The substance is designated as "$(+)$" or "d".

Compare to **levorotatory**

Diamagnetism. The weakest type of magnetic character. It is found in materials in which all of the **electrons** are paired. Because **covalent bonds** involve a **shared pair of electrons**, most substances are diamagnetic. An external **magnetic field** causes only a weak repulsion of a diamagnetic material.

Compare to **ferromagnetism, paramagnetism**

Diaphragm. A thin layer of **muscle** that separates the thoracic cavity from the abdominal cavity and functions in breathing.

Diastereomers. Any pair of **stereoisomers** that are not **enantiomers**. Diastereomers, unlike enantiomers, are chemically and physically different from one another. According to this definition, **geometric isomers** are considered diastereomers.

Also called diastereoisomers

Diastole. The period of the cardiac contraction cycle when the **atria** are filling and contracting. At the same time, the **ventricles** are relaxed and the **pressure** in the **aorta** is decreasing.

Dielectric. A material, or medium, that does not conduct electricity. In such a material, there are no free **electrons** because they are tightly bound to their respective atomic nuclei. When a dielectric is inserted between the plates of a **capacitor**, it decreases the net **electric field** in the capacitor and allows the **capacitance** to increase; thus, higher **voltages** can be applied without causing charge to pass across the gap.

Differentiation. A process whereby unspecialized **cells** change into more specialized cells, often during the process of becoming a **tissue**. The development is usually brought on by the asymmetrical distribution of **cytoplasm**, the action of chemical mediators (e.g., **cytokines**), and other changes induced by the surrounding environment; however, the exact mechanisms remain largely unknown.

Diffraction. The spreading of **waves** as they pass into the region behind an obstacle. The amount of diffraction depends on the size of the obstacle relative to the **wavelength** (i.e., the smaller the obstacle, the less diffraction there will be). Diffraction is an inherent property of waves, not particulate matter.

    Compare to **reflection, refraction**

Diffusion. The random movement of free **molecules**, **ions**, or particles in **solution** or suspension, under the influence of **thermal energy**, toward a uniform distribution throughout the available volume. Diffusion can also be considered as the movement of particles from an area of higher **concentration** to an area of lower concentration.

    See also **active transport, facilitated diffusion**

Digestion. The physiologic process of converting ingested food materials into nutritive **molecules** that are soluble and metabolically useful.

Dihybrid. An individual who is **heterozygous** for two given traits (i.e., the **genotype** may be represented by AaBb).

Dioptre (D). The unit that represents the refractive **power** (P) of a **lens**. It is equal to an inverse meter: $1 \text{ D} = 1 \text{ m}^{-1}$.

Diploid. Having two complete sets of **chromosomes** (in humans, 2 sets of 23 chromosomes each), that is, twice the number of chromosomes normally present in a **gamete**.

Dipole. An electric dipole is a pair of equal, but opposite, point charges separated by a finite **distance**. The dipole aligns with the **electric field** lines, as represented in *Figure 39*.

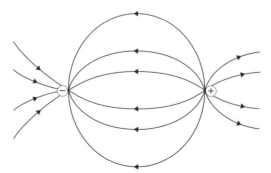

Figure 39. Electric dipole

Dipole moment (μ). The partial ionic character in **covalent bonds** between two **atoms** with different **electronegativities**. It is equal to the product of the magnitude of the charge at each center of charge (Q) and the distance separating the centers of charge (d), as represented by: $\mu = Qd$. The unit of the dipole moment is the debye (D).

> ✔ In **polar molecules**, the locations of the centers of charge develop according to the electronegativities of the atoms. For example, in gaseous HCl, the **electron** cloud is drawn toward the electronegative Cl end of the **molecule**. Thus, the Cl end is the negative center of charge and the H end represents the corresponding positive center of charge. Still, the Cl and H are not **ions**; the charges surrounding them are only fractions of the charges of an electron or **proton**.

Disaccharide. A **carbohydrate** composed of two **monosaccharides** connected by a covalent **glycosidic bond**. Some common examples are sucrose (**glucose**-α1,β1-fructose), lactose (galactose-β1,4-glucose), and maltose (glucose-α1,4-glucose).

> *See also* **anomers**

Dispersion. The separation of polychromatic light (white light that consists of many **frequencies**) into the full spectrum of light rays of different frequencies, which occurs when light passes through a prism. The phenomenon is due to the fact that **waves** of different frequencies are refracted to different degrees upon exiting the prism. The **index of refraction** (n) is greater for shorter **wavelengths**; therefore, in the visible spectrum, violet light is bent the most and red light is bent the least.

Displacement. The net change in the position of an object. This quantity involves both the direction and magnitude of the **distance** traveled (i.e., it is a **vector**) and is independent of the specific path taken. Displacement (d) is the shortest possible distance between two points *(Figure 40)*.

> *Compare to* **distance**

Figure 40. Displacement

Distal convoluted tubule. The portion of the **nephron** that leads into the **collecting tubule** where sodium **ions**, potassium ions, and chloride ions are actively reabsorbed into the interstitial **tissue** of the **kidney**. Similar to the ascending limb of the **loop of Henle**, it is impermeable to water and **urea**; thus, the **fluid** in the tubule becomes increasingly dilute.

Distance. A measurement of the length of the path between two points. It is a **scalar** because the value only has magnitude, not direction.

> *Compare to* **displacement**

Distillation. A method for the separation of mixtures of materials in which the various components have different **boiling points**. This process consists of preferential **evaporation** of the more volatile (i.e., lower boiling) components and **condensation** and collection of the resulting vapors in separate flasks.

Diverging lens. Any thin **lens** that is wider at the ends than at the middle. It refracts parallel incident light rays away from the axis, causing their divergence; however, the light rays seem to originate from a **focal point** (F) behind the lens *(Figure 41)*. The **focal length** (f) is always negative for a diverging lens. The image produced by a diverging lens is always a **virtual image**.

> *Also called* negative lens
> *See also* **lens equation**
> *Compare to* **converging lens**

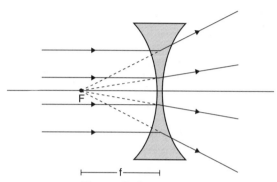

Figure 41. Diverging lens

Dominance. One **allele** in a pair is said to be dominant if its expression in a **heterozygous** individual results in the same **phenotype** as in an individual who is **homozygous** for the dominant allele. This allele could be **recessive** in relation to a third allele.

Doppler effect. A change in the observed **frequency** (f ′) of a **wave** when the source or the detector is moving relative to the medium in which the wave is propagating. As the source and detector move toward each other, the frequency becomes higher. As the source and detector move away from each other, the frequency becomes lower. The following equation can be used for all situations:

$$f' = f \left(\frac{v \pm v_d}{v \mp v_s} \right)$$

v = **velocity** of the wave
f = frequency of the wave at the source
v_d = velocity of the detector
v_s = velocity of the source

✔ In the equation, the upper signs (+, −) are used when the source and detector are moving toward each other and the lower signs (−, +) are used when the source and detector are moving away from each other.

Duodenum. The first section of the **small intestine** where most of the **protein, carbohydrate**, and **lipid** breakdown takes place.

> *See also* **intestinal villi**

E

Ectoderm. One of three primary **tissues** that forms during **gastrulation**. This tissue eventually gives rise to the **neural groove, neural tube, neural crest, epidermis, lens** of the eye, and linings of the mouth and anus.

See also **endoderm, mesoderm**

Efferent. Leading away from a particular origin (e.g., efferent **nerve impulse** traveling from the **brain**, efferent arteriole through which **blood** flows out of the **glomerulus**).

Compare to **afferent**

Effusion. The passage of **gas** through a tiny hole or pore.

Egg. The female **gamete**.

Ejaculation. The ejection of **semen** caused by a sympathetic nervous stimulation of **muscle** at the base of the **penis**.

Elastic collision. An interaction of matter during which there is conservation of **momentum** and **kinetic energy**. Both of the following equations apply:

Conservation of momentum:

$$m_1 v_1 + m_2 v_2 = m_1 v_1' + m_2 v_2'$$

Conservation of kinetic energy:

$$\tfrac{1}{2} m_1 v_1^2 + \tfrac{1}{2} m_2 v_2^2 = \tfrac{1}{2} m_1 v_1'^2 + \tfrac{1}{2} m_2 v_2'^2$$

m = mass
v = **velocity**

Elasticity. The property of a **solid** that determines the extent of its deformation upon application of a **stress** or **strain**.

Elastic modulus. See **Young's modulus**

Electric dipole. See **dipole**

Electric field. The conceptual region of space around a charged particle in which electrostatic forces act on all other particles in that space. An electric field exists around every charged particle and extends to an infinite **distance** from that particle. The magnitude of a field (E) at a particular point is defined as the **force** (F) per unit charge, as given in the equation:

$$E = \frac{F}{q}$$

q = a positive test charge at a particular point

A test charge is so small that it does not exert a measurable force of its own. At any point, the direction of the field is the direction of the force on the test charge. Another equation defining the magnitude of a field (E) at the distance (r) from a single point charge (Q) is:

$$E = k(Q/r^2)$$

$k \cong 9 \times 10^9 \text{ N} \cdot \text{m}^2/\text{c}^2$

See also **Coulomb's law**

Electric potential (V). The **potential energy** (PE) per unit charge (q), as given in the equation:

$$V = \frac{PE}{q}$$

Because only differences in potential energy are measurable, only the difference in electric potential (i.e., **potential difference**) is a measurable quantity. The unit of electric potential and potential difference is the **volt**.

✔ Electric potential is sometimes referred to as "potential" when "electric" is assumed.

Electrochemical cell. A device that allows a **redox reaction** to occur through a wire, as opposed to direct contact among the reagents. It converts chemical **energy** to electrical energy, thus serving as a source of electricity (see Appendix B, Figure 7). Although the reaction is spontaneous, its magnitude and direction depend on the particular chemicals at each **electrode**.

See also **battery, electrolytic cell, galvanic cell**

Electrode. A substance composed of metal (e.g., platinum) or carbon which, when placed in an ionic **solution**, serves as a medium where **electrons** may be exchanged.

See also **anode, cathode**

Electrolysis. A process whereby **electrons** are pushed into a system by an external **voltage** source in order to cause nonspontaneous reversals of electrochemical reactions. The process is commonly used for electroplating and recharging **batteries**.

See also **electrolytic cell**

Electrolyte. A substance that dissociates into **cations** and **anions** when dissolved in polar **solvents**.

Electrolytic cell. A device in which **electrolysis** occurs by applying an external **voltage**.

Compare to **galvanic cell**

Electromagnetic radiation. A special type of **wave** that is produced by an oscillating (vibrating) or accelerating electric charge. The radiation is propagated through space as **transverse waves**, which consist of an oscillating **electric field** and an oscillating **magnetic field** that are perpendicular to one another and to the direction of motion. The entire electromagnetic spectrum consists of a wide range of **frequencies** of electromagnetic waves (e.g., light, radio waves, gamma rays), all of which travel at a constant **speed** (3.00×10^8 m/s).

Electromagnetic wave. See **electromagnetic radiation**

Electromotive force (EMF). The difference in electric **potential energy** between the two **electrodes** of a **galvanic cell** (per unit charge). It is often calculated as the difference between the standard **reduction potentials** of the **anode** and **cathode**. The EMF is measured in volts. The value of the EMF ($\Delta\mathcal{E}°$) determines how the net cell reaction will proceed:

- if $\Delta\mathcal{E}° > 0$, the reaction proceeds as written
- if $\Delta\mathcal{E}° < 0$, the reaction proceeds in the reverse direction from how it is written
- if $\Delta\mathcal{E}° = 0$, no reaction occurs and no **current** flows between electrodes

   See also **cell potential, cell voltage**

Electromotive force (EMF) source. A device, such as a **battery**, that establishes and maintains a constant **voltage** in a conducting loop (**circuit**).

Electron. A subatomic particle that has a negative charge and is virtually massless (mass = $\frac{1}{1836}$ of the mass of a **proton**). It is the fundamental unit of electric charge.

   Compare to **neutron, proton**

Electron affinity (EA). The **energy** released (a negative value) when an **electron** is moved from infinity into the lowest vacant atomic orbital in a gaseous **atom**. The stronger the attraction, the higher the |EA|.

   ✔ Electron affinity has the same periodic table trends as **ionization energy**.

Electron configuration. The characteristic structure of the **electron** cloud of an **atom** or **ion** which minimizes the total **potential energy** of all the electrons.

   See also **atomic orbital**

Electronegativity. A measure of the relative attraction of a bonded **atom** for the **electrons** of the other atoms to which it is bonded.

Electron shell. A group of **atomic orbitals** within the same **energy** level [i.e., having the same **principal quantum number** (n)]. For example, the K shell consists of the $1s^1$ and $1s^2$ orbitals.

Electron transport chain. A series of **electron** carrier **molecules** that are embedded in the inner membrane of **mitochondria** in eukaryotic **cells**. As electrons are moved toward lower **energy** states, they release energy that is used to drive **protons** out of the mitochondrial matrix into the outer membrane. The protons travel through special proton pumping channels. This movement creates a **protonmotive force** (i.e., a **diffusion** gradient) that permits the chemiosmotic synthesis of **adenosine triphosphate** via **oxidative phosphorylation**.

Electrophile. A reagent with an incomplete outer **electron shell** that is attracted to an electron-donating species. Electrophilic reagents are most commonly added to compounds that contain double or triple bonds.

   See also **electrophilic addition, electrophilic aromatic substitution**
   Compare to **nucleophile**

Electrophilic addition. An **addition reaction** in which an **electrophile** [e.g., H^+ in a hydrogen halide (HX)] attacks the **pi bond** between carbon **atoms** in a double or triple bond, thus forming a **carbocation**. The reaction proceeds with the carbocation reacting with the **nucleophile** ($X-$) to form a methyl halide. The reaction usually follows **Markovnikov's rule**. This is the most common reaction involving **alkenes**, **alkynes** [e.g., the addition of HBr to propene *(Figure 42)*], and highly strained cyclic compounds.

$$CH_3CH = CH_2 \; + \; HBr \; \rightleftharpoons \; CH_3\overset{\overset{\displaystyle Br}{\displaystyle |}}{C}HCH_3$$

Figure 42. Electrophilic addition

Electrophilic aromatic substitution. A **substitution reaction** in which an **electrophile** replaces a hydrogen **atom** in an aromatic ring structure. It begins when delocalized **electrons** of the ring are attacked by the electrophile, resulting in the formation of a **resonance**-stabilized **carbocation**. The loss of H^+ completes the substitution. The aromaticity of the ring is retained in all products.

>   *See also* **meta-directing substituents; ortho, para-directing substituents**

Element. A substance that contains **atoms** having the same **atomic number**.

Elementary process. A single step in the overall path of a chemical reaction. If one **molecule** is involved, it is unimolecular; if two molecules are involved, it is bimolecular.

Elimination reaction. A type of chemical reaction in which **atoms** or **ions** are removed from a **molecule** to form products with either multiple bonds or ring structures.

Embryo. The developing human that comes into existence after successful **fertilization**. The term is applicable until the establishment of all major **organs** is complete, which occurs toward the end of the first trimester (approximately the third month). After this point, the developing human is referred to as a **fetus**.

Embryogenesis. The development of a mammal that begins after **fertilization** and continues until all major **organs** have been established (see Appendix A, Figure 6). The term is also commonly used to refer to the entire developmental process until birth.

Emission spectrum. The pattern of discrete **frequencies** of light (**photons**) that are emitted by a particular **atom** when its **electrons** jump from **excited states** to lower **energy** levels. The only photons that are emitted by a given **element** are those that have energies that exactly correspond to the difference in energy between the two atomic energy levels. The pattern can be observed as a series of bright bands when the light is analyzed with a spectroscope. The same frequencies that are emitted by an atom are also absorbed; therefore, the **absorption spectrum** exactly corresponds to the emission spectrum for a given element.

Empirical formula. The chemical formula that gives the ratio in which **atoms** are combined in a compound.

>   *Compare to* **molecular formula**

Emulsion. A colloidal suspension of two **liquids** that are not soluble in one another.

Enamine. A nitrogen-containing compound formed by the reaction between a secondary **amine** and a carbonyl-containing compound (e.g., **aldehyde**). The reaction proceeds via the formation of a carbinolamine and an iminium **ion**. A double bond forms between the carbons that are α and β to the nitrogen **atom** *(Figure 43)*.

   Compare to **imine**

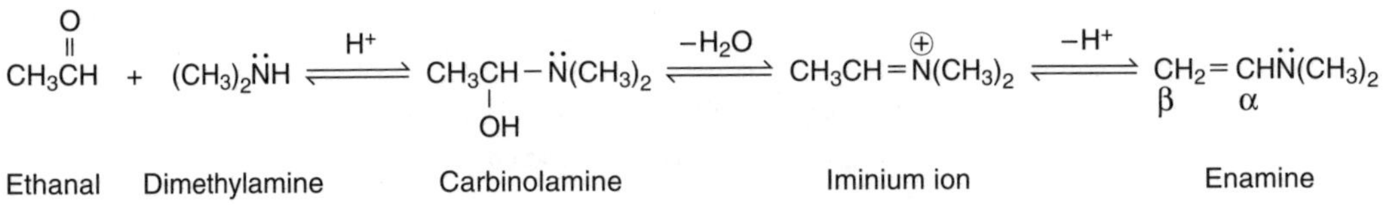

$$\underset{\text{Ethanal}}{\overset{\overset{\displaystyle O}{\|}}{CH_3CH}} + \underset{\text{Dimethylamine}}{(CH_3)_2\overset{..}{N}H} \overset{H^+}{\rightleftharpoons} \underset{\underset{\text{Carbinolamine}}{|}}{\underset{OH}{CH_3CH-\overset{..}{N}(CH_3)_2}} \overset{-H_2O}{\rightleftharpoons} \underset{\text{Iminium ion}}{CH_3CH=\overset{\oplus}{N}(CH_3)_2} \overset{-H^+}{\rightleftharpoons} \underset{\underset{\beta\quad\alpha}{}}{\underset{\text{Enamine}}{CH_2=CH\overset{..}{N}(CH_3)_2}}$$

Figure 43. Enamine formation

Enantiomer. One of a pair of **stereoisomers** that are NOT superimposable on their mirror images. Each of the two enantiomers rotates plane-polarized light in a given direction. The interchange of any two groups around a **chiral center** converts a compound to the opposite enantiomer.

   ✔ The term enantiomer implies a specific relationship between two compounds. It is impossible to look at a single compound and ask whether it is an enantiomer without referring to a second stereoisomer.

   Also called optical isomer
   See also **absolute configuration, chirality**

Endocrine gland. A ductless secretory **organ** that releases **hormones** into the circulatory system.

Endocytosis. The process by which **molecules** are surrounded and engulfed by the **plasma membrane**, forming an intracellular vesicle in which the material is trapped. **Phagocytosis** is the uptake of large **solid** particles; **pinocytosis** is the uptake of dissolved molecules.

Endoderm. One of the three primary **tissues** that forms during **gastrulation**. This tissue eventually gives rise to the gut, **liver, pancreas, gallbladder, lungs**, and certain **endocrine glands**.

   Compare to **ectoderm, mesoderm**

Endometrium. The inner lining of the **uterus** that thickens in response to stimulation by **estrogen** and **progesterone**. It is sloughed off during menstruation.

Endoplasmic reticulum (ER). A double-membrane network that runs throughout the eukaryotic **cell**. It serves as a means of intracellular transport and is a precursor for other membrane systems (e.g., **Golgi body**). There are two types of ER: rough and smooth. Rough ER contains **ribosomes** on its surface and is a site of **protein** synthesis. Smooth ER is not associated with ribosomes and has varied functions, including **steroid** synthesis.

Endothermic process. A chemical reaction that proceeds with a positive **enthalpy change** (i.e., requires an input of **energy**).

   Compare to **exothermic process**

Energy. The ability to do **work**. It is a **scalar**.

Enolate ion. A reactive **intermediate** generated from an **aldehyde** or **ketone**. This **resonance**-stabilized **salt** of a carbonyl-containing compound is formed by the deprotonation of the acidic α-hydrogen **atom** (i.e., on the carbon that is adjacent to the **carbonyl group**) due to the presence of dilute strong **base** in the **solution** (*Figure 44*).

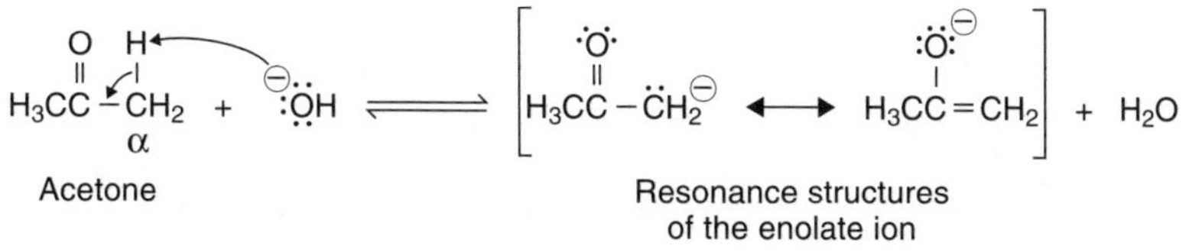

Acetone

Resonance structures
of the enolate ion

Figure 44. Enolate ion formation

Enterokinase. An activating **enzyme** that converts trypsinogen to its active form, trypsin, in the **duodenum**. Trypsin is a **protease**.

Also called enteropeptidase

Enthalpy change (ΔH). A measure of the amount of **heat** absorbed during a chemical reaction that occurs at a constant **pressure**. If the process is **endothermic**, ΔH is positive; if the process is **exothermic**, ΔH is negative.

Enthalpy of formation (ΔH$_f^°$). The **enthalpy change** for a reaction at 25°C and 1 atm in which 1 **mole** of the compound is formed from **elements** in their **standard states** (i.e., their most stable forms at 1 atm and a given **temperature**).

Also called standard **heat of formation**

Entropy (S). (1) A measure of the disorder of a thermodynamic system. (2) A measure of the amount of **energy** that has become unavailable for further **work** ("**heat** death").

✔ Entropy is a **state function**; it is constantly increasing in the system and surroundings and it is not conserved in a reaction.

Envelope. An outer coat that surrounds some **viruses** (e.g., HIV) and is rich in **protein, lipids**, and glycolipids.

Enzyme. A biochemical agent (almost always a globular **protein**) that catalyzes a specific synthesis or metabolic reaction by bringing two **substrates** into close proximity and proper orientation, thus lowering the **activation energy** required to create new chemical bonds. An enzyme is a biological **catalyst**; thus, it is not itself altered by the reaction.

✔ The enzyme activity is affected by any condition that changes the 3-dimensional shape of the protein, namely **temperature, pH**, osmolarity of the medium, and binding of **coenzymes**.

Epidermis. The outermost layer of skin, which is composed of stratified **epithelium** and is covered by a dead keratin layer. It contains a variety of **cell** types, including melanocytes and **macrophages**.

Epididymis. A long, coiled tube that is cupped around the **testes**. It serves as the site of **sperm** storage and maturation.

Epiglottis. The flap of **tissue** that prevents ingested material from travelling down the **trachea**.

Epimers. A pair of **diastereomers** that each have several **chiral centers**, but have opposite **configurations** at only one of the **chiral carbon atoms** [e.g., D-**glucose**, D-galactose *(Figure 45)*].

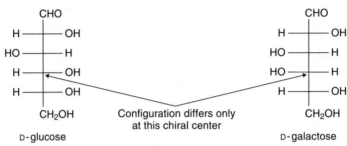

Figure 45. Epimers

Epinephrine. See **adrenaline**

Epithelium. A type of **tissue** that covers external surfaces (e.g., skin) or lines an internal cavity (e.g., gastrointestinal tract). Epithelial **cells** can serve protective, secretory, or absorptive functions. There are three structural classes of epithelial tissue:

1. Simple epithelium (contains a single layer of epithelial cells)
2. Stratified epithelium (contains several layers of epithelial cells that may or may not be covered by a layer of keratin, which is a strong and protective fibrous **protein**)
3. **Glands**

Epitope. A characteristic shape or location on the surface of an **antigen** where an **antibody** binds.

Also called antigenic determinant

Equilibrium constant (K). A value that describes the interrelationship of the components of a chemical reaction at the **equilibrium state** *(Figure 46)*.

For the reaction: $aA + bB \rightleftharpoons cC + dD$,

$$K = \frac{[C]^c \, [D]^d}{[A]^a \, [B]^b} \text{ at the equilibrium state}$$

Figure 46. Equilibrium constant

Equilibrium state. The point in a reaction system when the rate of the forward reaction equals the rate of the backward reaction. Commonly, the equilibrium state consists of a dynamic equilibrium in which the forward and backward reactions are actually proceeding despite their rates being equal. This is contrasted with a static equilibrium in which the rates of the forward and backward reaction are both zero. In both cases, however, the net rate of reaction is zero.

Equipotential surface. All points on the surface are at the same **electric potential** (i.e., there is no **potential difference** between them). The **electric field** is perpendicular to the surface at all points.

Equivalence point. The point in a **titration** at which the added reagent (e.g., **acid**) just neutralizes the other reagent (e.g., **base**), so that both reagents are present in an equal number of **moles**.

Erythrocyte. A circulating red blood **cell** that contains **hemoglobin** and, thus, serves as a **blood**-borne carrier of oxygen and carbon dioxide.

Erythropoietin. A **hormone** that stimulates the **bone marrow** to produce **erythrocytes**. It is secreted by specialized **cells** in the **kidneys**.

Esophagus. The tube that connects the **pharynx** to the **stomach**. No digestion takes place in the esophagus. Ingested material moves through the esophagus via **peristalsis**.

Ester. A compound formed when water is removed from an **acid** and an **alcohol**. For example, **carboxylic acid** esters contain the $-CO_2R$ group (R is either an **alkyl** or **aryl group**) and are usually formed by the reaction between a carboxylic acid and an alcohol.

> *See also* **esterification**

Esterification. The direct, **acid**-catalyzed reaction of a **carboxylic acid** with an **alcohol** that proceeds via a series of protonation and deprotonation steps. Basically, it is a **nucleophilic substitution** reaction that yields an **ester** and water *(Figure 47)*.

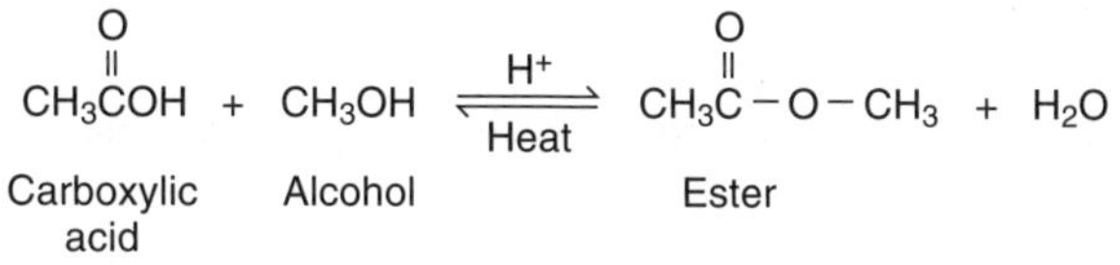

$$CH_3\overset{\overset{O}{\|}}{C}OH + CH_3OH \underset{\text{Heat}}{\overset{H^+}{\rightleftharpoons}} CH_3\overset{\overset{O}{\|}}{C}-O-CH_3 + H_2O$$

Carboxylic acid   Alcohol   Ester

Figure 47. Esterification

Estrogen. A major female sex **hormone** that is produced by the **ovary** upon stimulation by **follicle-stimulating hormone (FSH)** and which inhibits further production of FSH. In the **menstrual cycle**, estrogen stimulates the proliferation of **cells** of the **endometrium** and triggers the release of **luteinizing hormone**. Estrogen also affects female secondary sex characteristics.

Ether. An open-chain or cyclic compound in which two carbon **atoms** are bonded to a single sp^3-hybridized oxygen atom. An epoxide is a three-membered ring ether. Crown ethers are large ring systems with repeating units. Because the ether functional group (R-O-R') is fairly inert (unreactive), ethers are often used as organic (**hydrophobic**) **solvents**. They are cleaved only when treated with heated, concentrated **acid**, which causes a **nucleophilic substitution** reaction that yields an **alcohol** and an alkyl halide. Ethers are characterized by:

- polarity (less so than water or alcohols)
- the ability to undergo **hydrogen bonding** with water, alcohols, or **phenols**
- weak basicity due to the unshared **valence electrons** of the oxygen atom

✔ Diethyl ether (CH_3CH_2-O-CH_2CH_3) is a compound that is commonly called "ether" and has historically been an important anesthetic.

Eukaryote. A classifying term applied to a wide range of complex **cells** (including some unicellular organisms) that have characteristic membrane-bound **organelles**, including a **nucleus**.

Also called eucaryote
Compare to **prokaryote** (see Appendix A, Table 1)

Evaporation. See **vaporization**

Evolution. Progressive genetic change within a **population** that gradually occurs over a long period of time. Divergent evolution refers to changes in one species that lead to many new species. Convergent evolution refers to changes that occur in separate species and lead to one common species.

Excited state. The state of an **atom** when one or more **electrons** occupy **atomic orbitals** of **energy** higher than the lowest available to them. The excited state of an atom should be distinguished from the excited state of a **nucleus** (see the special note to **gamma ray**).

Compare to **ground state**

Exocrine gland. Any **gland** that releases its secretion through a duct; for example, digestive glands and sweat glands.

Compare to **endocrine gland**

Exocytosis. The export of **molecules** from the **cell**.

Compare to **endocytosis**

Exothermic process. A reaction that proceeds with a negative **enthalpy change** (i.e., produces **heat**).

Expiration. The expulsion of air from the **lungs**, which is normally a passive process due to the elastic recoil of the chest wall.

Compare to **inspiration**

Expiratory reserve volume. The amount of air that can be forcefully expired from the **lungs** after a normal **expiration**; it is normally just over 1 L.

See also **inspiratory reserve volume, residual volume, tidal volume, vital capacity**

Extensor. Any **skeletal muscle** that increases the angle of a joint.

Compare to **flexor**

External ear. The anatomical region of the ear that includes the **pinna** and the **auditory canal**.

Extracellular matrix (ECM). An elaborate network of **polysaccharides** and **proteins** that exists in the spaces between **tissue cells** (extracellular spaces). A familiarity with the ECM is most important in the discussion of **connective tissues**, in which the ECM is often more plentiful than the cells themselves. Examples of ECM include **collagen** fibers in **cartilage** and **blood plasma**.

Extraction. The isolation of a compound by treating a mixture with a **solvent** in which the desired component is selectively soluble or insoluble. The same effect can also be obtained by partitioning the mixture between two immiscible solvents of different polarities; one solvent is usually water and the other is usually an organic/**hydrophobic** solvent (e.g., **ether**). Ideally, the **solute** of interest is preferentially dissolved in one of the solvents while the impurities (i.e., other solutes) are largely dissolved in the other solvent. Often, the **acid/base** properties of the desired solute permit its extraction; for example, compounds with acidic **protons** (e.g., **alcohols**) are readily extracted out of organic solvents by the addition of an aqueous solution of a **weak base**. The resulting **salt** is water soluble and can be isolated by the **evaporation** of the organic phase or layer.

> ✔ A complete explanation of liquid-liquid extraction is beyond the scope of this book. However, it is important and you are encouraged to carefully review your textbooks, course notes, and laboratory manuals for the details.

F

Facilitated diffusion. The **diffusion** of **molecules** across a **plasma membrane** by way of specific **protein** channels that serve as a means of transport for molecules to which the membrane is otherwise impermeable (e.g., **monosaccharides** and **amino acids**). The process does not require **energy** and flow is always from a region of high **concentration** to a region of low concentration (i.e., down the concentration gradient).

> *Also called* passive transport
> *Compare to* **active transport, diffusion**

Facultative anaerobe. An organism that may function as an **aerobe** or **anaerobe**, depending on its environment.

Fallopian tubes. Tubes through which the **egg**, carried by waves of muscular contraction, travels from the **ovaries** to the **uterus**. **Fertilization** takes place in the fallopian tubes.

Family. A vertical column of the periodic table of **elements**. Each family is comprised of a group of elements with the same number of **valence electrons** and analogous **electron configurations**.

> *Also called* group

Faraday ($\mathcal{F}$). The electric charge on 1 **mole** of **electrons**, which is equal to 96,485 **coulombs**.

Faraday's law of electrolysis. Describes the relationship between the amount of electricity passed through an **electrolytic cell** and the mass (m) of material deposited at the **cathode**:

$$m = \frac{i \cdot t}{\mathcal{F}} \cdot M$$

> i = the **current** in **amperes** (C/s)
> t = the time in seconds
> $\mathcal{F}$ = a **Faraday** (9.65×10^4 C/mol)
> M = the **molecular weight** of the substance being deposited (g/mol)

Faraday's law of electromagnetic induction. States that an **electromotive force** is induced in a wire by a changing **magnetic field**.

> ✔ An **electric field** is always induced by a changing magnetic field, whether a wire is present or not.

> *See also* **Lenz's law**

Fats. **Solid** triglyceride **esters** that contain mostly saturated **fatty acids**.

Fatty acid. A long **hydrocarbon** chain that ends with a **carboxylic acid** group.

Feedback inhibition. The regulation of the level of a biochemical product (e.g., **enzyme, hormone**) in response to its own magnitude. The synthesis of the factor is inhibited by an increase in its **concentration**.

See also **allosteric ligands**

Fermentation. The process by which **cells** regenerate NAD^+ (a **reducing agent** that is necessary for **glycolysis**, but is in short supply in cells) in the absence of oxygen. Organic **molecules** (e.g., pyruvate) act as the final **electron** acceptors, resulting in the production of by-products such as lactic acid or ethanol.

See also **cellular respiration**

Ferromagnetism. The property of a material that refers to its high degree of intrinsic magnetism, which exists independently of external **magnetic fields**. Ferromagnetic materials have strong internal magnetic fields.

Compare to **diamagnetism, paramagnetism**

Fertilization. The fusion of **haploid gametes** to form a **diploid zygote**. In mammals, fertilization normally takes place in the **fallopian tubes**.

Also called syngamy

Fetus. The unborn, developing human in the **uterus** from approximately the second month of pregnancy until birth. The **embryo** becomes a fetus after the major **organs** have been initially established.

Fibroblast. Flat, branching **cells** that secrete **collagen** into the matrix between cells. This is the most common type of **connective tissue** cell.

First law of thermodynamics. In any process, the total amount of **energy** in the system and surroundings is conserved (i.e., energy is neither created nor destroyed). Within the system, the internal energy (E) is a **state function**. Changes in the internal energy are expressed as:

$$\Delta E = q + w$$

q = **heat** absorbed *by* the system
w = **work** done *on* the system

Also called law of conservation of energy

Fischer projection. A diagrammatical method of representation of the 3-dimensional stereo-chemistry (i.e., spatial orientations) around a **chiral center** (stereogenic carbon), in which vertical substituents face away from the observer and horizontal substituents face toward the observer *(Figure 48)*.

✔ Diagrams can be rotated 180°, but cannot be flipped or rotated by any other angle.

See also **absolute configuration, chirality**

Fission. A nuclear reaction in which a heavy **nucleus** splits into smaller nuclei with the release of large amounts of **energy**.

Compare to **fusion, def. (2)**

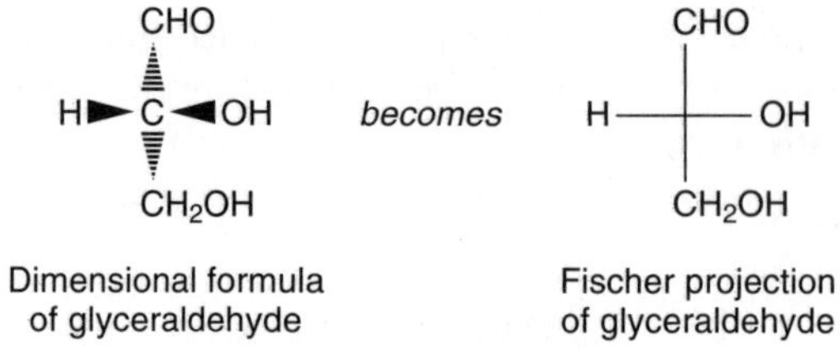

CHO

H►C◄OH   *becomes*   H ———— OH

CH₂OH

Dimensional formula   Fischer projection
of glyceraldehyde   of glyceraldehyde

Figure 48. Fischer projection

Flagellum. A long, hair-like **organelle** that projects out from the surface of a **cell** and is used for locomotion. In **bacteria**, it is composed of a single chain of **protein** subunits. In **eukaryotes**, it consists of a cylinder of **microtubules**.

Flat bone. A type of structural **bone** that primarily serves protective functions and is involved in little, if any, movement (e.g., skull, ribs, vertebrae). Flat bones are also the sites of much **blood cell** production.

Flexor. Any **muscle** that decreases the angle of a joint upon contraction.

Compare to **extensor**

Flotation. A phenomenon that occurs when the **buoyant force** on an object has a magnitude equal to the **weight** of the object. An object floats if its **density** is less than that of the **fluid**.

See also **Archimedes' principle**

Fluid. Any substance that can flow (e.g., **gas**, **liquid**). Fluids are characterized by:
- an inability to support any **shear stress**
- the capacity to exert **pressure** on an enclosed body [**forces** are perpendicular to all surfaces of the submerged object (see **bulk modulus**)]

Fluid mosaic model. See **plasma membrane**

Fluorescence. The property that allows an **atom** to emit **electromagnetic radiation** after it has absorbed a **photon** that brought it to an **excited state**. As the atom returns to its **ground state**, the **electrons** may fall back to lower **energy** levels in a series of two or more "jumps," thus emitting light at **wavelengths** that are longer (i.e., lower energy and **frequency**) than those of the light that was initially absorbed. Commonly, fluorescent materials emit visible light after absorbing ultraviolet light.

Foam. A mixture of a **gas** in a **liquid**.

Focal length (f). The **distance** between the **focal point** (F) and the center of a **lens** or mirror. For a mirror:

$$f = \frac{r}{2}$$

r = the radius of the sphere from which the curved mirror is theoretically derived

See also **concave mirror, converging lens, convex mirror, diverging lens**

Focal point (F). The point along the axis of a mirror or **lens** where the image of an object that is infinitely far away forms. It is the point at which parallel incident light rays reflected by the mirror or refracted by a **converging lens** converge and focus. The focal point is found at a **distance** from the mirror or lens called the **focal length**.

Follicles. Capsules in the **ovaries** in which the **eggs** develop.

Follicle-stimulating hormone (FSH). A gonadotrophic **hormone** that is released by the anterior **pituitary gland**. In females, FSH initiates the final stage of **egg** development in the **ovary** and causes the ovaries to produce **estrogen**. In males, FSH stimulates **spermatogenesis**.

Follicular cells. Supportive **cells** that surround the primary **oocytes** in the **ovary** during the **follicular phase**.

Follicular phase. The initial stage of the female reproductive cycle in which the development of **eggs** is initiated by **follicle-stimulating hormone (FSH)**. Because **estrogen** inhibits FSH production, the rise in estrogen levels marks the end of this phase.

> *See also* **luteal phase**

Force. The magnitude and direction of the action of one particle or object on another that may or may not cause motion of the latter (a **vector**). The magnitude of the force is related to the mass and **acceleration** of the object on which the force is acting, as described by **Newton's second law** (F = ma).

Forebrain. One of the three principal divisions of the **brain** that consists of the **hypothalamus**, **thalamus**, and **cerebrum**.

Formal charge. The charge assigned to an **atom** that is determined by assuming that one-half of the **electrons** in **shared pairs** and all of the **lone pair** electrons belong to that atom. The sum of the formal charges on all of the atoms in a **molecule** is zero; in an **ion**, the sum equals the ion's charge.

> ✔ The formal charge does not usually represent the actual charge on the atom.

Fovea. The area of the **retina** with the highest concentration of **cones** and, thus, the highest visual sensitivity.

Free energy (G). The **energy** in a reaction that remains available for future **work**. Systems tend toward lower energy and, therefore, toward lower free energy. The change in free energy (ΔG), which is a **state function**, is the total change in the amount of usable energy resulting from a chemical reaction, as given by the equation:

$$\Delta G = \Delta H - T\Delta S$$

ΔH = the **enthalpy change** (i.e., the change in total energy)
 T = absolute **temperature**
ΔS = the change in **entropy** (i.e., the change in the amount of unavailable energy)

Because ΔG is a function of both ΔH and ΔS, it combines two properties that represent the tendencies of spontaneous reactions: the tendency toward lower energy and the tendency toward increased entropy. Therefore, ΔG can be used to predict the direction of a spontaneous reaction:

- If $\Delta G < 0$, then the reaction is spontaneous
- If $\Delta G > 0$, then the reverse reaction is spontaneous
- If $\Delta G = 0$, then the system is at equilibrium and no net reaction will occur
  The standard free energy ($\Delta G°$) applies when all reagents are in their **standard states** and is related to the **equilibrium constant** (K) by the following equation:

$$\Delta G° = -RTlnK$$

R = universal **gas** constant
T = absolute temperature

Also called Gibbs free energy

Free-fall motion. Motion due to the **force** of **gravity**, which is vertical with respect to the earth.

Free radical. Any **atom** that has one or more unpaired **electrons**. Free radicals are highly reactive and, under normal conditions, are nonisolatable intermediates in chemical reactions. They are also associated with **deoxyribonucleic acid** mutation and food spoilage. Like **carbocations**, free radicals are stabilized by substituents (e.g., **alkyl groups**) that release electrons to the central carbon atom. Consequently, the order of free-radical stability parallels that of carbocations; methyl radicals ($\cdot CH_3$) are the least stable and tertiary radicals ($\cdot CR_3$) are the most stable (where R is an electron-donating substituent).

✔ A carbon atom with an unpaired **valence electron** is written as $\cdot C$.

Freezing point. The **temperature** at which a **liquid** is converted to a **solid**, or vice versa. This is the same temperature as the melting point.

Freezing point depression (ΔT_f). The decrease in the **freezing point** of a **liquid** that occurs upon addition of a **solute**. The freezing point of a **solution** (**solvent** and solute) is always lower than the freezing point of the pure solvent. This is a **colligative property**.

See also **boiling point elevation**

Frequency (f). The property of a **wave** that indicates the number of **wavelengths** that pass a given point per unit time. The frequency is related to the wavelength (λ) and **velocity** (v) of the wave by the equation: $v = \lambda f$.

Friction. A **force** that resists the motion of a body and is due to the direct contact between two **solid** surfaces. The force acts directly opposite to the direction of motion and is proportional to the **normal force** (N) between the two surfaces, yet is independent of the area of contact:

$$F_f = \mu N$$

μ = a constant of proportionality that is dependent on both surfaces

✔ There are two types of friction: kinetic, involving a body in motion, and static, involving a body at rest.

Functional residual capacity (FRC). The amount of air that remains in the **lungs** after normal **expiration** and before the next **inspiration** (i.e., between breaths). It cannot be directly determined; however, it can be calculated using indirect methods. The average FRC is approximately 2.5 L.

See also **residual volume, tidal volume**

Fundamental frequency. The lowest **resonant frequency** for a given string or pipe, as given by the following equations:

$$f = \frac{v}{2L}$$

v = the **velocity** of the **wave**
L = the length of a string or open pipe

$$f = \frac{v}{4L}$$

L = the length of a closed pipe (i.e., closed at one end)

See also **harmonics**

Fungi. A kingdom (in the Whittaker 5-kingdom system) of eukaryotic, filamentous, heterotrophic decomposers that do not contain chlorophyll (i.e., they are not plants). Yeasts are single-celled fungi.

✔ Heterotrophic decomposers produce their **energy** by degrading the organic **molecules** of dead plants and animals.

Fusion. (1) The conversion of a **solid** to a **liquid** at the **freezing point**. (2) Nuclear fusion is a nuclear reaction whereby small nuclei combine to form a larger, heavier **nucleus**, resulting in the release of **energy**. This is the principal reaction that permits **heat** formation on the sun.

G

Gallbladder. A small **organ** that is adjacent to the **liver** and stores excess secreted **bile salts**. **Cholecystokinin** stimulates the gallbladder to empty its contents into the **duodenum**.

Galvanic cell. An **electrochemical cell** that produces a **current** and a **voltage** by means of **oxidation** and **reduction** reactions when the electrodes at which these reactions take place are connected with an electrical **conductor**. It converts chemical **energy** to electrical energy, thus serving as a source of electricity (see Appendix B, Figure 7). The reaction is spontaneous; its magnitude and direction depend on the particular chemicals at each electrode. A common example is a lead storage **battery**.

> *Also called* voltaic cell

Gamete. A **haploid cell** (e.g., **spermatozoon**, **egg**) that permits sexual reproduction by fusing with another gamete of the opposite sex.

Gamma ray. High-**energy** and high-**frequency photons** (i.e., **electromagnetic radiation**) that are released when a **nucleus** of a decaying **atom** undergoes transitions from **excited states** to **ground states**. Gamma rays have zero mass.

> ✔ The available energy levels of a nucleus are much farther apart than those of **atomic orbitals**; therefore, the photons released when an excited nucleus drops to its ground state have much higher energies than those that are released when **electrons** drop back to their ground states, as seen in the **emission spectrum** of an **element**.
>
> *Compare to* **alpha particles, beta particles**

Ganglion. A cluster of **nerve cell** bodies in the **peripheral nervous system**.

> *Compare to* **nucleus, def. (3)**

Gap junction. A type of intercellular junction that permits the exchange of **ions** and small **molecules** between the **cytoplasm** of adjacent **cells**. This junction provides a means of electrical "coupling" of cells. For example, **nerve impulses** are quickly transmitted throughout **cardiac muscle** via gap junctions, which permits the coordinated contractions that are characteristic of cardiac muscle cells.

Gas. A **fluid** state of matter in which the **molecules** are separated by large **distances** and are in random motion. Gases have **densities** that are typically 500–1000 times smaller than their corresponding **solids**. They are characterized by:

- high compressibility
- low intermolecular **forces**
- indefinite potential for expansion
- complete filling of the entire volume of their containers

> *See also* **ideal gas**

Gastrin. A **hormone** that regulates the **pH** of the **stomach** by controlling the secretion of hydrochloric acid (HCl).

> ✔ The secretion of HCl is also controlled by the **parasympathetic nervous system**, via the **vagus nerve**.

Gastrula. The term that refers to the **embryo** after the **blastula** has undergone development involving the formation of an **archenteron**; a blastopore, which is an opening to the archenteron; and the primary **tissues** (**ectoderm**, **endoderm**, and **mesoderm**).

Gastrulation. The stage of **embryogenesis** in which the **blastula** becomes a **gastrula**.

Gene. A **deoxyribonucleic acid (DNA)** sequence that either encodes a single **messenger ribonucleic acid**, **transfer ribonucleic acid**, or **ribosomal ribonucleic acid molecule**, or regulates the **transcription** of another DNA sequence. Genes are the functional units of heredity.

> *See also* **locus**

Gene flow. The movement of **genes** from one **population** to another.

Gene frequency. The proportion of individuals in a **population** who carry a particular **gene**.

> *Compare to* **allele frequency**

Gene pool. The collection of all the **alleles** present in a given **population**.

Genetic drift. The random loss of **alleles** from a **population** and the consequent change in **allele frequency** in that population. This phenomenon occurs mainly in small populations.

Genome. The total collection of all **genes** that exist in the **chromosomes** of a single organism.

Genotype. The genetic constitution in a single organism that determines the nature of a specific trait. The term can also be used to refer to the total genetic makeup of an organism.

> *Compare to* **phenotype**

Geometric isomers. A subclass of **diastereomers** in which the **isomers** differ in that substituents are on the same or opposite sides of a site of rigidity (i.e., they only differ in their **configurations**). This type of isomerism exists in **alkenes**, in which the site of rigidity is the double bond, and in cyclic compounds.

> *Also called cis-trans* isomers

Gibbs free energy. See **free energy**

Gland. A **tissue** or **organ** that releases chemical substances into the **blood** stream (**endocrine**) or onto internal or external surfaces of the body (e.g., intestinal tract surface, skin) [exocrine].

Glial cell. A nonconducting support or companion **cell** that is associated with a **neuron**.

> *See also* **Schwann cell**

Glomerulus. A network of **capillaries** in **Bowman's capsule** that filter **blood** to allow substances such as water, **glucose**, **proteins**, and **ions** to enter the **nephron**.

Glucagon. A **hormone** produced by the **pancreas** that raises the **concentration** of **glucose** in the **blood** by stimulating the breakdown of **glycogen** into glucose in **muscles** and in the **liver**.

> *Compare to* **insulin**

Gluconeogenesis. The process by which **glucose** is formed from lactate and pyruvate, which are products of **glycolysis**. It occurs primarily in the **liver**.

Glucose. The most common **monosaccharide** in humans. It is the most widely used fuel **molecule** and is necessary for life because it is the only fuel that can be used by the **neurons** in the **brain**.

Glycerol. A three-carbon **molecule** with three **hydroxyl groups** that forms the backbone of certain **lipid** molecules.

> *See also* **fat, phospholipid**

Glycogen. A branched **polysaccharide** that is a storage form of **glucose** in animal **cells**.

Glycogenesis. The production of **glycogen** from **glucose**.

Glycolysis. The anaerobic **biochemical pathway** that permits **adenosine triphosphate (ATP)** synthesis by substrate-level phosphorylation as well as the formation of NADH from NAD$^+$, which can later be used as a **reducing agent** in the chemiosmotic synthesis of ATP in **oxidative phosphorylation**. Glycolysis serves as the first stage of aerobic **respiration** and takes place in the **cytoplasm**. When oxygen is unavailable, glycolysis is completed by a series of reactions known as **fermentation**.

Glycosidic bond. A link between the carbon 1 of one **monosaccharide** and an —OH group of another (**acetal** bond), which forms a **disaccharide** *(Figure 49)*. This bond is either a 1,4-α or 1,4-β linkage depending on the stereochemistry at the anomeric carbon 1 that is involved in the bond.

> *See also* **anomer**

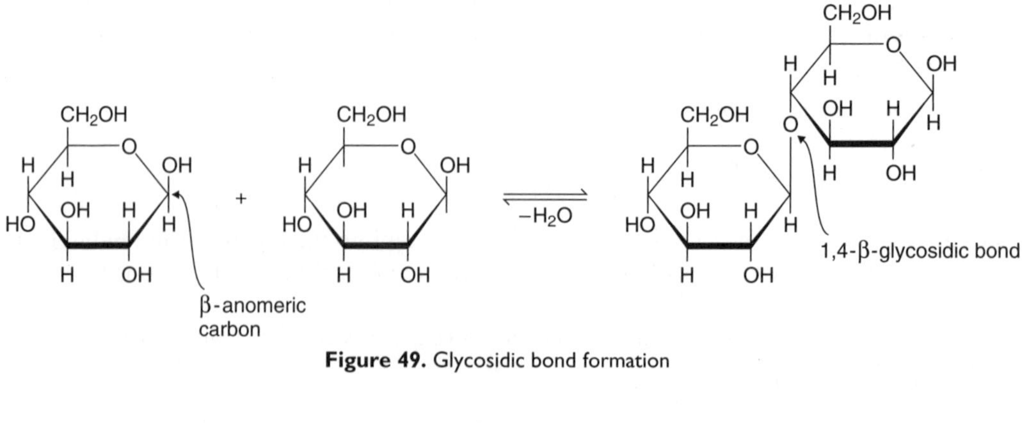

Figure 49. Glycosidic bond formation

Glycosylation. The addition of sugar groups to another type of **molecule**.

Golgi body. A collection of smooth, flattened membranes within a **cell** where packaging and secretion of **proteins**, glycoproteins, and other substances is initiated. **Glycosylation** of proteins and the synthesis of **polysaccharides** also takes place here. These membranes may be continuous with the **endoplasmic reticulum** at certain points.

Graham's law of effusion. The relative rates of **effusion** of two **gases** at the same **temperature** are inversely proportional to the square root of their **molecular weights**:

$$\frac{\text{rate of gas 1}}{\text{rate of gas 2}} = \frac{\sqrt{M_2}}{\sqrt{M_1}}$$

✔ This experimental observation was theoretically confirmed by the mathematical derivations of the **kinetic molecular theory of gases**.

Gravity. A **force** of attraction that the earth has for objects close to its surface. The force of gravity is directed toward the surface of the earth and is equal to the **weight** (w) of an object:

$$F_g = w = mg$$

m = mass of the object
g = **acceleration** due to gravity = 9.81 m/s^2 for any object (use 10 m/s^2 on the MCAT)

✔ Gravity is actually associated with all matter in the entire universe; even **atoms** exert gravitational attractive forces on one another.

Gray matter. The **nerve cell** bodies and **dendrites** of the nervous system.

Compare to **white matter**

Ground state. The state of lowest possible **energy**, which occurs when all the **electrons** in an **atom** are in the lowest energy levels available. The ground state implies stability of an atom.

Growth hormone. See **somatotropin**

H

Half-cell. A single **electrode** and the **solution** in which it is immersed.

> *See also* **electrochemical cell, electrolytic cell, galvanic cell**

Half-life. The time it takes for half of the initial amount, or **concentration**, of a reacting material to decay or to be used up in a reaction.

Half-reaction. One of the **oxidation** or **reduction** reactions in a **redox reaction** system. Corresponding half-reactions cannot occur independently.

Halogenation. A general type of reaction that is either an **electrophilic addition** reaction, in which a halogen (e.g., chlorine, bromine) is added across a double or triple bond, or a **substitution reaction**, in which the halogen replaces hydrogen **atoms** in an **alkane**. The substitution reaction proceeds via the formation of **free radical** intermediates and requires light or **heat**; the products depend on the relative stabilities of the **alkyl radical**.

Haploid. Refers to the condition of having only one set of **chromosomes**, as opposed to pairs of **homologous chromosomes**. **Gametes** are haploid.

> *Compare to* **diploid**

Hardy-Weinberg equilibrium. A theoretical prediction that in a closed, sexually-reproducing **population**, the proportions of dominant and recessive **allele frequencies** remain constant from one generation to the next. The equilibrium is represented by the following equation:

$$p^2 + 2pq + q^2 = 1$$

p = **frequency** of dominant **allele**
q = frequency of recessive allele

> ✔ Five factors produce deviation from this equilibrium: genetic mutation, migration, **genetic drift**, non-random mating, and selection (artificial or natural).

Harmonics. The **natural frequencies** of a pipe or string that are integral multiples of the **fundamental frequency**. In comparison, an overtone is any of the natural frequencies other than the fundamental. The fundamental is referred to as the first harmonic and the first overtone is called the second harmonic. When not specifying a particular harmonic, the terms overtone and harmonic are basically synonymous.

Haversian canals. Narrow channels in **compact bone** that carry **blood vessels** and **nerves**.

Heart. The muscular pump that causes circulation of the **blood** throughout the body *(Figure 50).*

> *See also* **cardiac muscle**

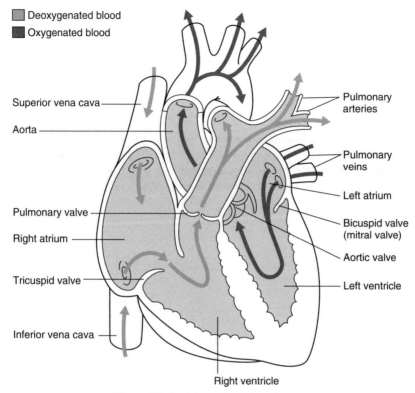

Figure 50. Circulation through the heart

Heat. The **energy** that is due to the random motion of **molecules** moving between a system and its surroundings or between two bodies or objects. Heat is not an intrinsic property of a system, as opposed to **enthalpy**, **entropy**, and **temperature**; therefore, its magnitude depends on the manner in which the transfer takes place.

See also **heat flow**

Heat capacity. See **molar heat capacity** and **specific heat**

Heat flow. A net transfer of **energy** due to a difference in **temperature** between a system and its surroundings. This flow occurs by **conduction**, **convection**, or **radiation**. The **heat** lost by one body is equal to the heat gained by another (**conservation of energy**). By convention, heat flow out of a system is negative, and heat flow into a system is positive.

Heat of formation. See **enthalpy of formation**

Heat of fusion (ΔH_{fus}). The quantity of **heat** required to convert one **mole** of a given **solid** into one mole of **liquid** at constant **temperature** (i.e., the melting point) and **pressure**.

Heat of vaporization (ΔH_{vap}). The quantity of **heat** required to convert one **mole** of a given **liquid** into one mole of **gas** at constant **temperature** (i.e., the **boiling point**) and **pressure**.

Helper T cells. **T lymphocytes** that incite and mediate both **cell-mediated** and **humoral immune responses** when presented with an **antigen** and simultaneous stimulation via **cyto-**

kines. Helper T cells are critical **cell** mediators of specific immunity. In AIDS, it is helper T cells that are primarily infected and eventually killed by HIV. Consequently, both the humoral and cell-mediated immune responses are severely crippled.

Hematocrit. The percentage of the whole **blood** volume that is **erythrocytes**; it is approximately 45% in humans.

Hemiacetal. A **molecule** that contains an **ether** and a **hydroxyl group** on the same carbon. It is formed by the addition of one **alcohol** molecule to an **aldehyde** or a **ketone** *(Figure 51)*. In cyclic hemiacetals, the alcohol group on carbon 4 or 5 adds to the **carbonyl group** of carbon 1 of the same molecule [e.g., **glucose** *(Figure 52)*].

See also **anomers**

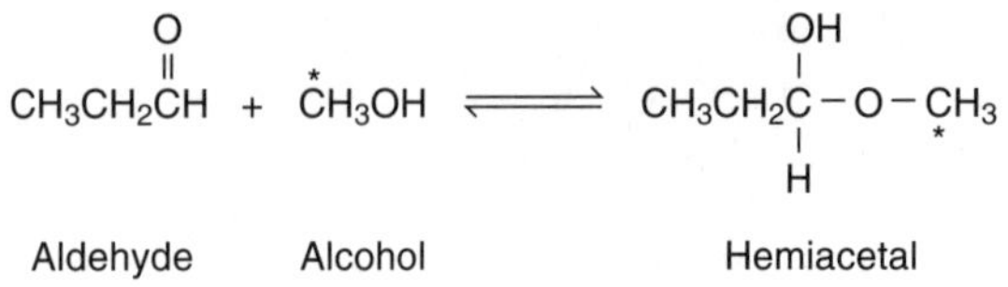

$$CH_3CH_2\overset{\overset{\displaystyle O}{\|}}{C}H \ + \ \overset{*}{C}H_3OH \ \rightleftharpoons \ CH_3CH_2\overset{\overset{\displaystyle OH}{|}}{\underset{\underset{\displaystyle H}{|}}{C}} - O - \overset{*}{C}H_3$$

Aldehyde   Alcohol   Hemiacetal

Figure 51. Hemiacetal formation

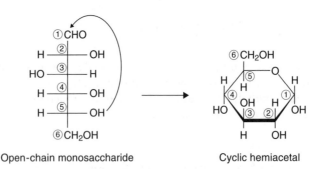

Open-chain monosaccharide   Cyclic hemiacetal

Figure 52. Cyclic hemiacetal formation

Hemoglobin. A **protein** that is contained in **erythrocytes** and is composed of four **polypeptide** chains (globin), each of which is bound to an iron (Fe^{2+})-containing **molecule** called heme. Each heme subunit reversibly binds one oxygen molecule; thus, hemoglobin transports oxygen to the **tissues**. Heme also binds to carbon dioxide, which it transports from the tissues to the **lungs**, and carbon monoxide. Because carbon monoxide has the highest affinity (i.e., ability to bind) for hemoglobin, exposure to large quantities of this **gas** can be fatal because it inhibits further binding of oxygen.

See also **Bohr effect**

Hemopoiesis. The formation of the circulating **blood cells** (**erythrocytes, leukocytes, platelets**) from undifferentiated hemopoietic **stem cells** in the **bone marrow**.

Also called hematopoiesis

Henderson-Hasselbach equation. A formula that permits the calculation of the **pH** of a **buffer solution**:

$$pH = pK_a + \log\left(\frac{[\text{base}]}{[\text{conjugate acid}]}\right)$$

pK_a = negative logarithm of the **acid** dissociation constant = $-\log K_a$
[base] = molar concentration of the **base**
[conjugate acid] = molar concentration of the conjugate acid

Henry's law. The **partial pressure** (P_a) of a **gas** above a **solution** is directly proportional to the amount of that same gas that is dissolved in the solution:

$$P_a = k_a X_a$$

k_a = a constant of proportionality that depends on both the gas and the **solvent**
X_a = the **mole fraction** of the **solute** (the gas) in solution

Hess's law of constant heat summation. Because **enthalpy change** (ΔH) is a **state function**, a reaction carried out at constant **temperature** and **pressure** undergoes the same ΔH regardless of the path that is taken. In practical terms, this means that ΔH can be calculated for a reaction simply by summing ΔH for any series of reaction steps that collectively represent the desired chemical change. The easiest way to do this is to make use of known **enthalpies of formation** in the following equation:

$$\Delta H° = \Sigma\Delta H_f°(\text{products}) - \Sigma\Delta H_f°(\text{reactants})$$

Heterozygote. An individual who is **heterozygous** for a given trait.

Heterozygous. The state of having two different **alleles** for a given trait.

Compare to **homozygous**

Hindbrain. One of the three principal divisions of the **brain**. It consists of the **cerebellum**, the **pons**, and the **medulla oblongata**, and is mainly responsible for coordinating motor reflexes.

Homologous chromosomes. See **homologous pair**

Homologous pair. One each of the maternal and paternal **chromosomes** that carry **genes** that code for the same traits.

Also called homologous chromosomes, homologues

Homologous structures. Anatomical structures that have evolved from a common structure, although their functions may differ.

Homozygote. An individual who is **homozygous** for a given trait.

Homozygous. The state of having identical **alleles** for a given trait on each member of a **homologous pair**.

Compare to **heterozygous**

Hooke's law. Describes a restoring **force** (F_r) that a spring exerts to bring itself back to its equilibrium position, as given by the following equation:

$$F_r = -kx$$

k = the spring constant (a measure of the stiffness of a given spring)

x = the change in the length of the spring from its equilibrium position

The negative sign implies that the restoring force acts in the direction opposite to the **displacement** of the spring.

See also **simple harmonic motion**

Hormone. A regulatory chemical that is made at one location and effects at a different location in the body, which is often a relatively large **distance** away from the source (see Appendix A, Table 2). Hormones (e.g., **proteins, steroids**) are the functional products of the **endocrine** system and produce a slow response relative to the nervous system.

Huckel's rule. For a compound to be **aromatic**, it must be planar, monocyclic, and have $4n + 2$ delocalized **pi electrons**.

Humoral immune response. A **specific immune response** that is mediated primarily by **antibodies** and is most often directed at extracellular pathogens (e.g., pathogenic **bacteria**) which, when bound by antibodies, become tagged for destruction.

Compare to **cell-mediated immune response**

Hund's rule. When **atomic orbitals** of the same shape and **energy** are available, **electrons** occupy each orbital with parallel spins until all of the orbitals are "half-filled;" only then are electrons paired with opposite spinning electrons in the same orbital.

See also **electron configuration**

Hybrid atomic orbitals. A combination of valence (outer) s, p, and sometimes d **atomic orbitals** in a single **atom**. The number of hybrid orbitals that form is always equal to the number of atomic orbitals that hybridized to form them; for example, two sp hybrid orbitals form when one s and one p hybridize. The formation of sp, sp^2, and sp^3 hybrid orbitals can be used to explain the bonding patterns and geometry in organic **molecules**.

- sp-Hybridization is associated with carbon atoms bonded to two other atoms, one of which is bonded via a carbon-carbon triple bond. The atoms across the triple bond are at 180° to one another.
- sp^2-Hybridization is associated with carbon atoms bonded to three other atoms, one of which is bonded via a carbon-carbon double bond. The geometry around the carbon is a trigonal planar shape.
- sp^3-Hybridization is associated with carbon atoms that are bound to four other atoms via single bonds. The shape around the carbon is that of a tetrahedron.

Hydration. The combination of any substance with water. In the case of an **alkene** in strongly acidic **solution**, a **molecule** of water adds across a carbon-carbon double bond to yield an **alcohol**.

See also **electrophilic addition, Markovnikov's rule**

Hydrocarbon. A **molecule** that consists entirely of carbon and hydrogen **atoms**. In saturated **hydrocarbons** (**alkanes**), all carbons are sp^3-hybridized; thus, there are only single bonds. In unsaturated hydrocarbons (**alkenes, alkynes**), some carbon atoms are sp- or sp^2-hybridized; thus, there are some double or triple carbon-carbon bonds.

Hydrogenation. The addition of hydrogen across carbon-carbon multiple bonds in the presence of a metal **catalyst** (e.g., platinum, nickel).

Hydrogen bonding. Weak intermolecular attraction (stronger than **van der Waals forces**) due to the interaction between partially positive hydrogen **atoms** that are bonded to **electronegative** atoms, such as C, F, N, or O. This is the type of bonding that occurs in **base pairs** in the **deoxyribonucleic acid** duplex.

Hydrohalogenation. An **electrophilic addition** reaction in which a hydrogen halide (HX), such as HCl or HI, is added across a carbon-carbon double bond to produce a haloalkane (RX), such as chloromethane.

Hydrolysis. The cleavage of a substance as the result of its reaction with water, such as the breakdown of **polymers** into dimeric or monomeric units.

> *Compare to* **condensation reaction**

Hydrophilic. A term that literally refers to a **molecule's** attraction to water, but is commonly used to refer to all **polar molecules** or molecules that are soluble in polar **solvents** (e.g., water).

> *Compare to* **hydrophobic**

Hydrophobic. A term that literally refers to a **molecule's** "fear" of water, but is commonly used to refer to all **nonpolar molecules** or molecules that are insoluble in water, but are soluble in nonpolar organic **solvents** (e.g., benzene).

> *Compare to* **hydrophilic**

Hydrostatic pressure. A **fluid pressure** generated by the **force** of the heartbeat that tends to push **plasma** and **molecules** out of the **capillaries** and into the **tissue** space.

> *Compare to* **oncotic pressure**

Hydroxyapatite crystals. A crystal complex (e.g., Ca^{2+}, PO_4^{3-}, and other **ions**) that is deposited in a **collagen** matrix during the construction of **bone**.

Hydroxyl group. The —OH group, which is the functional group that defines **alcohols**, **phenols**, and so forth.

Hyperosmotic. Refers to a **hypertonic solution** that has a greater **osmotic pressure** than a solution to which it is being compared (i.e., it has a higher **concentration** of **solutes**), regardless of whether or not the solutes can permeate through a membrane separating the two solutions.

> *See also* **hypertonic**
> *Compare to* **hypoosmotic**

Hypertonic. Refers to a **solution** that has a higher **concentration** of impermeable **solutes** as compared to another solution. Impermeable solutes cannot pass through a membrane separating the two solutions, thus differentiating a hypertonic solution from a **hyperosmotic** solution.

> *Compare to* **hypotonic**

Hyphae. The vegetative and reproductive filaments of **fungi**.

Hypoosmotic. Refers to a **hypotonic solution** that has a lower **osmotic pressure** than a solution to which it is being compared (i.e., it has a lower **concentration** of **solutes**), regardless of whether or not the solutes can permeate through a membrane separating two solutions.

> *Compare to* **hyperosmotic**

Hypothalamus. The portion of the **forebrain** that coordinates many of the functions of the **autonomic nervous system**, such as behavior, hunger, thirst, and sex drive. It also synthesizes **hormones**, such as **vasopressin** and **oxytocin**.

Hypotonic. Refers to a **solution** that has a lower **concentration** of impermeable **solutes** as compared to another solution. Impermeable solutes cannot pass through a membrane separating the solutions, thus differentiating a hypotonic solution from a **hypoosmotic** solution.

> *Compare to* **hypertonic**

Ideal gas. A low-**density gas** with no intermolecular **forces** and in which the individual **molecules** occupy zero volume. Although ideal gases do not really exist, they approach existence at high **temperatures** and low **pressures**.

See also **ideal gas law, van der Waals' equation**

Ideal gas law. The state of an **ideal gas**, as given by the following equation:

$$PV = nRT$$

P = the **pressure** of the **gas**
V = the volume the gas occupies
n = the number of **moles** of the gas
R = the universal gas constant = 0.08212 L · atm/K · mole
T = the **temperature** of the gas (in Kelvin)

Ileum. The third section of the **small intestine** where absorption of vitamin B_{12} and **bile salts** takes place.

See also **duodenum, jejunum**

Imine. A nitrogen-containing organic compound that is characterized by a carbon-nitrogen double bond and is formed by an **acid**-catalyzed addition-elimination reaction involving a primary **amine** or ammonia and a **carbonyl**-containing compound. The first step is the **nucleophilic addition** of the amine to the carbonyl carbon; the second step is the protonation of the **hydroxyl group**, which is then lost as H_2O in an **elimination reaction** (Figure 53). Unsubstituted imines (i.e., those formed from ammonia) are fairly unstable; however, substituted imines (i.e., those formed from primary amines) are quite stable.

Compare to **enamine**

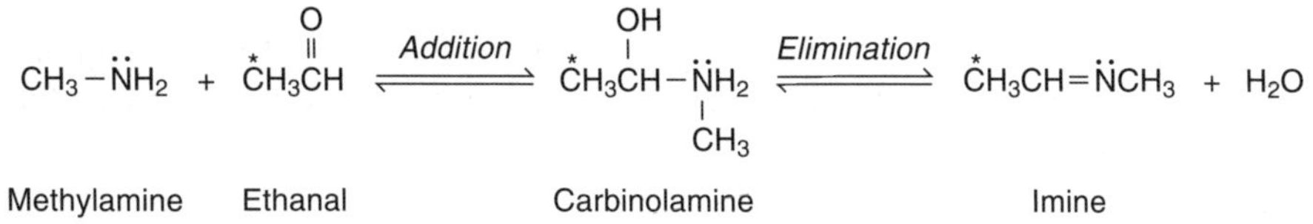

Figure 53. Imine formation

Immune response. The body's defensive reaction to a specific foreign substance, often marked by the production of **antibodies** directed against a specific **antigen** (see Appendix A, Figure 16).

See also **cell-mediated immune response, humoral immune response**

Immunoglobulin. See **antibody**

Impulse (Δp). The total change in **momentum** (p). It is equal to the product of the **force** (F) and time (t) required to cause the given change in momentum:

$$\Delta p = F \cdot \Delta t$$

✔ Impulse is a **vector** with the same units as momentum.

Incomplete dominance. The relationship between two different **alleles** for one **gene** that are simultaneously expressed in a **heterozygote**. The resulting **phenotype** is a mixture of the different phenotypes that would have resulted if either allele had been present in a **homozygous** condition (e.g., a pink flower results from a cross between a white flower and a red flower).

Compare to **codominance**

Independent assortment. See **law of independent assortment**

Index of refraction (n). The ratio of the **speed of light** in a vacuum (c) to the speed of light in a given medium (*v*), as given by:

$$n = c/v, \; n \geq 1$$

✔ The index of refraction is usually given at a particular **wavelength** because it varies slightly with the wavelength (except in a vacuum).

Indicator. A compound that changes color at the **equivalence point** in a **titration**; therefore, it can be used to indicate when the equivalence point has been reached.

Induction. (1) Embryogenetic induction is an alteration in the course of **tissue** development and **differentiation** due to the influence of an adjacent tissue. (2) Electrical induction is a charge redistribution in an object caused by a charged object in close proximity and resulting in net charge regions.

Compare to **conduction, def. (2)**

Inelastic collision. An interaction of matter in which there is a conservation of **momentum**, but not a conservation of **kinetic energy (KE)**. Some of the KE is transformed into **heat** or **potential energy** (there is always a conservation of total energy). A completely inelastic collision is a collision in which the two objects stick to one another.

Compare to **elastic collision**

Inertia. The tendency of a body or object to resist changes to its state of rest or motion, unless a net **force** causes the change. Mass is one measure of inertia; the greater the mass, the greater the resistance to motion.

See also **Newton's first law of motion**

Infrared spectroscopy. A laboratory method for the determination of molecular structure through the measurement of the infrared region of the **absorption spectrum** of a compound. The absorption of infrared radiation, which is a form of **electromagnetic radiation**, does not provide enough **energy** to boost **electrons** into higher energy levels, but instead causes increased **amplitudes** of vibration in the intramolecular bonds. The absorption of energy from the beam of transmitted radiation causes a decrease in the number of **photons** in the beam (i.e., a decrease in the intensity of the radiation). The magnitude of this decrease is what is measured in infrared spectroscopy. Different types of bonds can be distinguished using this method because each absorbs a characteristic **wavelength** of infrared radiation.

See also **nuclear magnetic resonance spectroscopy**

✔ The details of infrared spectroscopy are beyond the scope of this book; however, you should be comfortable with the different types of bond vibrations and the interpretation of the infrared spectra of compounds with common functional groups.

Inner ear. The anatomical structure that is comprised of the bony and membranous passageways that form the **cochlea**.

See also **middle ear, external ear**

Inspiration. The intake of air caused by the contraction of the **diaphragm,** as it moves downward, and the lifting of the **rib cage**.

Compare to **expiration**

Inspiratory capacity. The maximum amount of air that can be brought into the **lungs** after normal **expiration** has occurred. It is equal to the **tidal volume** plus the **inspiratory reserve volume** (approximately 3.5 L).

Inspiratory reserve volume. The extra amount of air than can be inspired over and above the normal **tidal volume** (approximately 3 L).

See also **expiratory reserve volume**

Insulator. A substance that does not readily conduct electricity (e.g., wood, rubber).

Compare to **conductor**

Insulin. A **hormone** produced by the **pancreas** that lowers **blood glucose** levels by inducing both the uptake of glucose by **cells** and the formation of **glycogen** in **muscle** and the **liver**.

Compare to **glucagon**

Intensity, sound. The physical property of a sound **wave** that is sensed as the loudness of the **sound**. Intensity is measured in watts/meter^2 (W/m^2) and is the **energy** transported by a wave per unit time across a unit area; it is proportional to the square of the wave **amplitude**. Because of the enormous range of intensities detectable by humans, the sound level (β), using a scale based on the decibel (dB), is a more practical measure of intensity:

$$\beta = 10 \log \left(\frac{I}{I_o}\right)$$

I = the intensity
I$_o$ = the standard reference intensity (usually taken to be 1.0×10^{-12} W/m^2, the threshold of human hearing)

Intensive properties. Properties of a substance that are not dependent on the amount of material present (e.g., **temperature**, **density**).

Compare to **colligative properties**

Intercalated disc. A junctional complex between two **cardiac muscle** cells that has several functions: it contains **gap junctions**, which allow synchronization of **cell** contractions; it attaches cardiac muscle cells to one another via **desmosomes**; it anchors the **actin** thin filaments, and is thus analogous to the Z-lines in **skeletal muscle** cells.

Interference. The interaction of two or more **waves** when they pass through the same space at the same time. The result is the summation (**superposition**) of the individual **displacements** of the different waves.

> *See also* **constructive interference, destructive interference**

Interferons. A group of **cytokines** that increase the resistance of **cells** to viral infection and stimulate **macrophage** and **natural killer cell** activity. They are secreted by a variety of cell types, including **helper T cells** and macrophages.

Intermediate filaments. Stable, insoluble cytoskeletal fibers that maintain the shape and integrity of the **cell**, especially at sites of mechanical **stress** (e.g., the skin). They are linked among adjacent cells via **desmosomes**.

> *See also* **cytoskeleton**
> *Compare to* **microfilaments, microtubules**

Intermediate species. A substance that is transiently formed during one step of a chemical reaction, but is quickly used up in a subsequent step. Intermediates do not appear in the stoichiometric equation. They are usually very short-lived, yet can be isolated under proper experimental conditions. In a plot of the changes in **potential energy** during a reaction, the formation of an intermediate corresponds to a slight depression in the curve relative to an **activated state**.

Intermolecular forces. **Forces** of attraction that exist between nonbonded **atoms** or **molecules**.

> *Compare to* **intramolecular forces**

Interneuron. A **neuron** in the **central nervous system** that relays **impulses** from one neuron to another, or to several other neurons.

Interphase. All the stages of the **cell** life cycle (G_1, S, and G_2 stages), excluding **mitosis** (see Appendix A, Figure 2). The G_1 phase is the cell's major growth stage. During the S phase, the chromosomal **deoxyribonucleic acid** is replicated. Throughout most of the interphase, the **chromosomes** are fully extended and uncoiled and are, therefore, not visible under the light microscope. During the G_2 phase, the chromosomes begin to condense into compact structures, which is a process that continues throughout **prophase**.

Interstitial cells. The **cells** in the **testes** that produce **testosterone**.

> *Also called* Leydig cells

Intestinal villi. Projections of the **mucosa** into the lumen of the **small intestine** that increase the surface area on which the absorption of nutrients takes place.

Intima. The layer of endothelial **cells** that line the interior of **blood vessels**.

> *Compare to* **adventitia, tunica media**

Intramolecular forces. The **forces** of attraction between bonded **atoms** in a single **molecule**.

> *Compare to* **intermolecular forces**

Intrapleural fluid. The water in the thoracic cavity that surrounds both **lungs**.

Ion. An **atom** that has lost or gained one or more **electrons**.

> *See also* **anion, cation**

Ionic bonding. The attractions between **ions** with opposite charges (i.e., metal and nonmetal), which form a lattice (network) that is electrically neutral (i.e., an **ionic compound**).

Ionic compound. A lattice (network) of **ions** with negative and positive charges in a ratio that renders the substance electrically neutral. Ionic compounds do not consist of true **molecules**; however, the smallest unit is defined in terms of the **empirical formula** of the compound.

> *Compare to* **molecular compound**

Ionization energy. The **energy**, per **mole** of a **gas**, required to remove a **valence electron** from a gaseous **atom**. Ionization is always **endothermic** (positive ΔH). On the periodic table of **elements**, it increases left to right and decreases top to bottom.

Ion product of water (K_w). The **equilibrium constant** for the self-ionization reaction of water. At 25° C:

$$K_w = [H_3O^+][OH^-] = 1.0 \times 10^{-14} \ M^2$$

> ✔ This value is used to calculate $[H_3O^+]$ and $[OH^-]$ in any dilute aqueous **solution**.

> *See also* **pH**

Iris. A "shutter" between the **cornea** and the **lens** of the eye that controls the amount of light that enters the **pupil**. It is a ring-like, pigmented **muscle** that differs in color between individuals.

Islets of Langerhans. The clusters of **endocrine cells** in the **pancreas** that produce **insulin** and **glucagon**.

Isoelectric point. The **pH** at which a particular **amino acid** carries no net charge.

Isomers. Chemical compounds that have the same **molecular formula**, but differ in their structural **conformations** or **configurations** (see Appendix B, Figure 4).

Isotonic. Refers to two **solutions** that have equal **tonicity**; thus, there is no net **diffusion** between the solutions if they are separated by a semi-permeable membrane.

Isotopes. Atoms of the same **element** that have the same **atomic number** but different **atomic masses**.

J

Jejunum. The middle section of the **small intestine** where the final breakdown of nutrients takes place before the **monosaccharides, amino acids,** and **fat molecules** are absorbed.

See also **duodenum, ileum**

β-keto acid. A **carboxylic acid** in which the β carbon is double-bonded to oxygen (this is a **carbonyl group**). **Decarboxylation** of a β-keto acid produces a **ketone**.

β-keto ester. An **ester** in which a **ketone** carbonyl group is β to the ester **carbonyl group**. It is most commonly formed in a **condensation reaction** between two esters *(Figure 54)*.

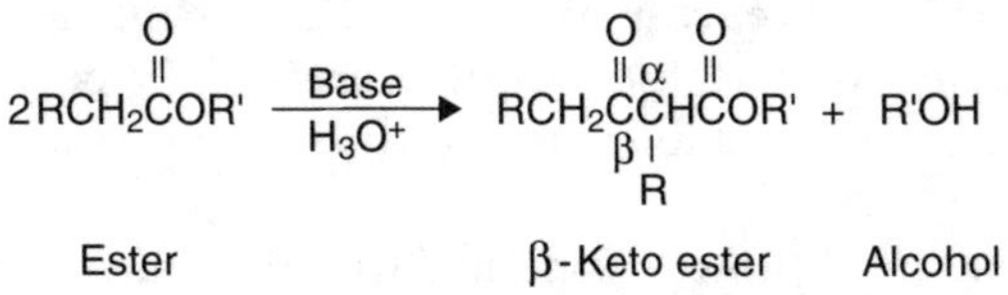

$$
2\,RCH_2COR' \xrightarrow[\text{H}_3\text{O}^+]{\text{Base}} RCH_2CCHCOR' + R'OH
$$

Ester   β-Keto ester   Alcohol

Figure 54. Formation of a β-keto ester

Ketone. An organic **molecule** in which a **carbonyl group** is bonded to two carbon **atoms** *(Figure 55)*. Its physical properties are similar to those of **aldehydes**.

> *See also* **acetal, tautomerism**

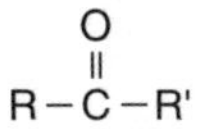

$$
R-C-R'
$$

Figure 55. Ketone

Kidneys. A pair of **organs**, the functional unit of which is the **nephron**, that serve an important homeostatic function by acting as the central regulator of body **fluid** composition. In addition to controlling **urine** composition, specialized kidney **cells** secrete **erythropoietin** and **renin**, both of which are compounds that serve endocrine functions.

> ✔ Recall that homeostasis is the maintenance of a relatively stable physiological state.

Kinetic energy (KE). A form of **energy** that is associated with the motion of objects:

$$
KE = \tfrac{1}{2}mv^2
$$

m = the mass of a body
v = the **velocity** of the motion of the body

Kinetic molecular theory of gases. A theory that describes the **energy** characteristics of **ideal gases** by analyzing the motion and mass characteristics (e.g., **force**, **momentum**) of the individual gas **molecules**. The theory is based on a set of postulates and assumptions about the nature of **gases**:

1. A pure gas is composed of a large number of identical molecules.
2. The volume occupied by a single molecule is negligible compared to the total volume occupied by the gas.
3. The gas molecules are in constant, random, and rapid motion.
4. The molecules do not exert any forces on one another.
5. The **pressure** that a gas exerts against the walls of a container is due to the collisions between the walls and the constantly moving gas molecules.
6. The interactions between any two molecules and between the molecules and the walls of a container are **elastic collisions**.

From these postulates, we can derive a form of **Boyle's law**:

$$PV = \tfrac{2}{3}nE_k$$

P = pressure of the gas
V = volume of the gas
n = the number of **moles**
E_k = the translational **kinetic energy** of 1 mole of gas (translational kinetic energy is that which is associated solely with the **displacement** of the object in a straight line, as opposed to the energy used for actions such as rolling or sliding)

Kinetochore. The chromosomal **protein** associated with the **centromere** to which the **spindle fibers** attach during **mitosis** or **meiosis**.

Krebs cycle. A cyclical series of aerobic cellular reactions in which the oxidized product of **glycolysis** (acetyl coenzyme A, formed by the **oxidation** of pyruvate) is sequentially oxidized to CO_2. The **energy** derived from the process is used to produce **adenosine triphosphate** (from ADP and P_i) and **reducing agents** ($NADH/FADH_2$ from NAD^+/FAD^+), compounds that ultimately enter the **electron transport chain**.

Also called citric acid cycle, tricarboxylic acid cycle

Labia. The folds of **tissue** that cover the opening to the **vagina**.

Lagging strand. The daughter **deoxyribonucleic acid (DNA)** strand that is synthesized discontinuously during DNA **replication**. Because the replication process only uses one **enzyme** (**DNA polymerase**), **nucleotides** can only be added to the 3′-OH end of a **nucleic acid molecule**. Therefore, the strand growing in the 3′ to 5′ direction must be synthesized as small pieces of DNA, called Okazaki fragments, which are individually synthesized in the 5′ to 3′ direction and are then ligated to one another to form the complete lagging strand.

 Compare to **leading strand**

Laminar flow. See **streamline flow**

Larynx. The **organ** found between the **pharynx** and the **trachea** that is responsible for the voice (voice box).

Lateral magnification (m). The enlargement of an image relative to an object due to a spherical mirror or a thin **lens**. It can be calculated using the following equation:

$$m = \frac{h_i}{h_o} = -i/o$$

 h_i = the height of the image
 h_o = the height of the object
 i = the **distance** from the image to the lens or mirror (the minus sign is a convention)
 o = the distance from the object to the lens or mirror

 ✔ The following sign conventions apply to mirrors and lenses:

 1. The object distance (o) is positive if the object is on the same side of the mirror or lens from which the light is coming (the object distance is always positive for a mirror).
 2. The image distance (i) is positive for **real images**, and negative for **virtual images**.
 3. Object and image heights are positive for points above the axis (this axis runs perpendicular to and at the midpoint of the mirror or lens), and negative for points below the axis.
 4. A positive magnification indicates an upright image, and a negative magnification refers to an inverted image.

 See also **concave mirror, converging lens, convex mirror, diverging lens, lens equation, mirror equation**

Law of independent assortment (Mendel's second law). For **genes** that are located on different **chromosomes**, or are so far apart on a chromosome that **recombination** occurs frequently, segregation of one **allelic pair** occurs independently of the other pairs during **meiosis**.

 See also **segregation (Mendel's first law)**

Law of reflection. The angle of incidence (Θ_i) of a **wave** equals the angle of reflection (Θ_r) *[Figure 56].*

✔ Remember that the angle is always that which is between the light ray and the normal.

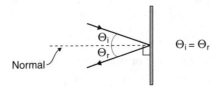

Figure 56. Law of reflection

Leading strand. The daughter **deoxyribonucleic acid (DNA)** strand that is synthesized continuously in the 5′ to 3′ direction during DNA **replication**.

Compare to **lagging strand**

Le Chatelier principle. When a stress is applied to a system in a dynamic **equilibrium state**, the system will always react in a direction that will tend to counteract or minimize the effect of the applied stress. A **buffer** provides a good example of this principle.

Lens. (1) A transparent material that causes the **refraction** of light. (2) In the eye, the lens completes the focusing of the light that has passed through the **cornea** into the eye. The shape of the lens is controlled by **ciliary muscles**.

See also **accomodation, converging lens, diverging lens**

Lens equation. The formula that relates the image **distance** (i) to the object distance (o) and the **focal length** (f):

$$\frac{1}{o} + \frac{1}{i} = \frac{1}{f}$$

✔ Notice that the lens equation is exactly the same as the **mirror equation**.

See also **converging lens, diverging lens, lateral magnification**

Lenz's law. An induced **current** will exist in a direction such that its **magnetic field** will oppose the external magnetic field that caused the induction.

✔ Lenz's law accompanies **Faraday's law of electromagnetic induction**.

Leukocyte. The general term for all white **blood cells** that patrol and defend the body against foreign particles. **Neutrophils** and **lymphocytes** are the most abundant, but there are also small amounts of eosinophils, basophils, and **monocytes**.

Levorotatory. Refers to the **enantiomer** that rotates plane-polarized light to the left (counterclockwise, negative). The compound is designated "(−)" or "*l*".

Lewis acid. See **acid**

Lewis base. See **base**

Leydig cells. See **interstitial cells**

Ligament. A type of **connective tissue** that holds **bone** together at the joints.

Limiting reagent. In a reaction, the compound with the least number of **moles** available to react. The limiting reagent is completely used up in the reaction while the other reagents remain in excess.

Linear momentum (p). See **momentum**

Linked traits. **Alleles** for different traits that are so close together on the same **chromosome** that they do not follow Mendel's **law of independent assortment.**

Lipase. A digestive **enzyme** that breaks up **lipids** and **fats** into smaller, absorbable **molecules.**

Lipid. A nonpolar, **hydrophobic** organic **molecule** that is insoluble in water (e.g., **fats**, **oils**, **steroids**, **phospholipids**).

Lipid bilayer. See **plasma membrane**

Liquid. A **fluid** state of matter in which **molecules** move freely with respect to one another. Because of intermolecular **cohesion**, a liquid does not expand indefinitely as a **gas** does. The **density** of a liquid is usually somewhat lower than that of its corresponding **solid.**

Liquid solution. A homogeneous, **liquid** mixture consisting of two or more miscible components (i.e., components that are capable of being mixed in any proportion).

Liver. The body's largest internal **organ** that serves as the principal mediator of metabolic activities. Its many functions include **blood-glucose** regulation, **glycogen** storage, **vitamin** and mineral storage, **protein** synthesis, cholesterol production, detoxification (e.g., **alcohol metabolism**), and the breakdown of blood-borne metabolites. It also produces **bile salts**, which are required for **lipid** absorption in the **small intestine.**

> ✔ The largest *external* organ is the skin. It accounts for roughly 15% of a person's body weight, while an adult's liver only weighs approximately 3 pounds.

Locus. The position on a **chromosome** of a specific **gene** or **transcription** unit.

Lone pair. A pair of **valence electrons** that are not involved in bonding.
> *Compare to* **shared pair**

Long bone. A **bone** involved primarily in locomotion and, therefore, typically found in extremities such as the hands, arms, and feet. The middle portions (shafts) of long bones are composed of **compact bone** surrounding an interior of **spongy bone.**
> *Compare to* **flat bone**

Longitudinal wave. A **wave** in which the direction of the vibration of the particles in the medium is the same as the direction of propagation of the wave (e.g., **sound** waves). A longitudinal wave causes a series of **condensations** (**compressions**) and **rarefactions** (expansions) in the medium.

✔ Think of the motion of a slinky as it shortens and lengthens.

Compare to **transverse wave**

Loop of Henle. The central portion of the **nephron** that has two distinct regions with virtually opposite functions.

- The descending limb is highly permeable to water, but relatively impermeable to **solutes**. The **diffusion** of water out of the lumen results in an increased **concentration** of solutes in the tubular **fluid**.
- The ascending limb is where the reabsorption of sodium chloride (NaCl) occurs; however, the membranes are highly impermeable to water, resulting in the dilution of the tubular fluid. It is the active reabsorption of **ions** by the ascending limb that raises the osmolarity of the interstitial fluid. This, in turn, causes the diffusion of water across the permeable membranes of the descending limbs (this is the basis of the counter-current multiplier system theory). Ultimately, the fluid in the loop of Henle becomes **hypoosmotic** (more dilute) as compared to **plasma**.

✔ The loop of Henle actually has three regions. For our purposes, we can consider the final portion (the thick ascending limb) as a part of the **distal convoluted tubule** because the functions of the two sections are very similar.

Lung. One of a pair of major **organs** that permit the intake of oxygen and the expulsion of carbon dioxide (ventilation, breathing) and the exchange of oxygen and carbon dioxide between the inspired air and the **blood**. The functional units of the lungs are the **alveoli**.

Luteal phase. The "second" stage of the female reproductive cycle that begins when **estrogen** stimulates the secretion of **luteinizing hormone (LH)**. LH then inhibits further estrogen production and causes the **follicle** to rupture, releasing the **egg** into a **fallopian tube** (**ovulation**). The ruptured follicle becomes the **corpus luteum**, which begins to secrete **progesterone**, a **hormone** that leads to development of the **endometrium** in preparation for pregnancy.

See also **follicular phase**

Luteinizing hormone (LH). A **hormone** produced by the **anterior pituitary gland** upon stimulation by **estrogen**. It induces **ovulation** and inhibits further estrogen production. In males, this hormone triggers the secretion of **testosterone**.

Lymph. The **fluid** that forms as **blood** is filtered out of the **capillaries** and into the **tissue** space. This fluid is drained from the tissues by the **lymphatic vessel system**.

Lymphatic vessel system. An auxiliary, open system of vessels that carries **leukocytes** and extracellular **fluids** (including blood **proteins**) back from the **tissues** into the general **blood** circulation. It is an important component of the immune system because the flow of **lymph** through the **lymph nodes** provides a means of **antigen**-presentation to the **lymphocytes**. The vessels also transport **fat** from the **small intestine** to the blood. Other components of this system include the **spleen**, tonsils, and **thymus**.

Lymph nodes. Fluid "filters" through which **lymph** flows before returning to the **blood** stream. The nodes are composed primarily of **B lymphocytes** and **T lymphocytes**. These lymphocytes are placed in direct contact with circulating **antigens**; thus, the lymph nodes are primary sites of **immune response** development.

Lymphocyte. A type of **leukocyte** found in the **blood** and the **lymph** that confers specific immunity against foreign particles.

> *See also* **B lymphocytes, T lymphocytes**

Lysis. The bursting or rupturing of a **cell** that results in cell death. It can be caused by a **virus**, chemical, **hyperosmotic** medium, **complement**, or **cytotoxic T lymphocyte** activity.

Lysogenic cell. A bacterial **cell** in which a **prophage** persists.

Lysosome. A membrane-bound eukaryotic cell **organelle** that contains digestive **enzymes** (**acid** hydrolases), which can be used to destroy foreign ingested particles or worn-out **cell** components.

M

Macrophage. A phagocytic, mononuclear **cell** that is derived from **bone marrow** and is found in **tissues,** as opposed to circulating in the **blood**. These cells engulf and digest foreign substances and then display **antigens** on their cell surfaces for facilitated recognition by **lymphocytes**.

> *See also* **monocyte**

Maculae, vestibular. Special sensory regions of the **utricle** and the **sacculus** that confer sensitivity to changes in the orientation of the head with respect to **gravity** and linear **accelerations** of the body.

> *See also* **semicircular ducts**

Magnetic field (B). A region of three-dimensional space in which a **magnetic force** acts. The field is produced by moving charges or moving **electric fields** and is perpendicular to the flow of charge.

> ✔ Use right-hand-rule #1 by imagining that you are grasping the wire so that your thumb points in the direction of the current and your fingers encircle the wire. Your fingertips point in the direction of the magnetic field.

Magnetic force (F_B). A **force** that is perpendicular to the direction of the **magnetic field** and acts at a right angle to a wire that is carrying a **current** *(Figure 57)*. The magnitude of the force on the wire is given by:

$$F_B = iLB\sin\theta$$

    i = the current
    L = the length of the wire
    B = the magnitude of the magnetic field

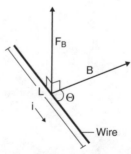

Figure 57. Magnetic force

The force on a single moving charge is given by:

$$F_B = qvB\sin\theta$$

q = the magnitude of the charge
v = the **velocity** of the charge
B = the magnitude of the magnetic field

✔ Use right-hand-rule #2 by pointing your outstretched fingers in the direction of the current and pointing your thumb (at a right angle to your fingers) in the direction of the magnetic force while the palm of your hand faces in the direction of the magnetic field.

Magnetic quantum number (m_l). The component of an **electron configuration** that describes the spatial direction and orientation of an **atomic orbital**. This value is limited by the **angular momentum quantum number** (l). The magnetic quantum number can have any integral value from $-l$ to $+l$; therefore, there are ($2l + 1$) values of m_l for each value of l.

Malonic acid. A potent inhibitor of the **Krebs cycle**.

Also called malonate

Markovnikov's rule. In the **electrophilic addition** of a hydrogen halide (HX) to an unsymmetrical **alkene** (i.e., the groups bonded to the two double-bonded carbon **atoms** are different), the H^+ always goes to the side of the double bond where the most hydrogens are already present. The regioselectivity (i.e., the predominance of one product) of this reaction is explained by **carbocation** formation, in which the **nucleophile** binds to the carbon atom that most effectively stabilizes the positive charge of the carbocation.

Mass number. The sum of the number of **protons** and the number of **neutrons** in a given **atom**.

Mechanical wave. See **wave**

Media. See **tunica media**

Medulla oblongata. A component of the **hindbrain** that controls functions such as breathing and arterial **pressure**.

✔ In general terms, the medulla is the interior portion of an **organ** (e.g., **adrenal medulla**, renal medulla).

Meiosis. Reductional **cell** division (called reduction-division) in which a single **diploid** cell becomes four **haploid** cells via two successive nuclear divisions (see Appendix A, Figure 4). This process only occurs in cells that produce **gametes** (i.e., **spermatocytes** and **oocytes**). In the first nuclear division (meiosis I), **homologous pairs** of **chromosomes** are separated, each homologue consisting of a pair of sister **chromatids**. In the second nuclear division (meiosis II), the **centromeres** split and the sister chromatids are separated from one another. **Deoxyribonucleic acid replication** only occurs before meiosis begins; it does not occur between the two nuclear divisions.

✔ The stages of meiosis II are similar to the stages of **mitosis**.

Compare to **mitosis**

Membrane potential. The voltage across the **plasma membrane** of a **cell**, the magnitude and direction of which depend on the distribution of charged **ions** on either side of the membrane. By convention, the direction of the **electric potential** is described in terms of the charge on the inner surface of the membrane.

See also **action potential, resting potential**

Mendel's first law. See **segregation of alleles**

Mendel's second law. See **law of independent assortment**

Meninges. The membranes that cover the **brain** and **spinal cord**. There are a total of three membranes: the dura mater (outer membrane), arachnoid layer (middle layer), and pia mater (inner membrane).

Menstrual cycle. The female reproductive cycle of **egg** production and release and endometrial thickening, which results in periodic **menstrual flow** when pregnancy has not taken place. The cycle takes approximately 28 days.

Menstrual flow. The monthly shedding of **blood** and the **endometrium** when pregnancy has not occured.

Also called menses

Meso compound. An organic compound with at least two equivalently-substituted **chiral centers** that are symmetrically arranged *(Figure 58)*, thus implying that it has an internal plane of symmetry. Such a compound can be superimposed on its mirror image and, therefore, is not optically active. When meso forms of compounds are possible, the number of **stereoisomers** of that compound is less than 2^n (n = the number of chiral carbons).

Compare to **enantiomer**

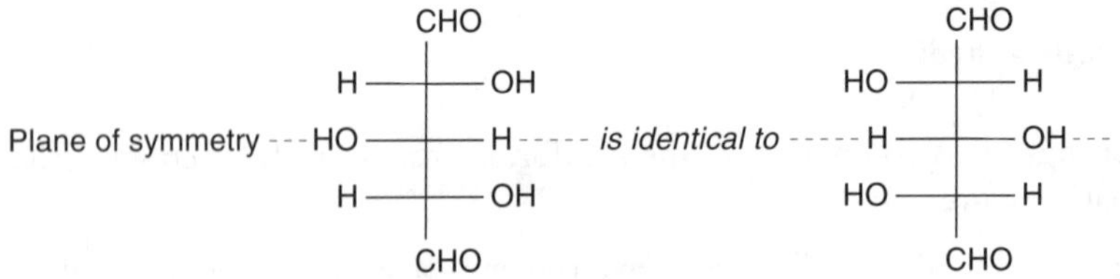

Figure 58. Meso compound

Mesoderm. One of the three primary **tissues** that forms in the **gastrula** during **embryogenesis**. This layer gives rise to the **notochord**, skeleton, **muscles**, circulatory system, reproductive system, and excretory system (e.g., **kidneys**).

Compare to **ectoderm, endoderm**

Mesosome. An invagination in the **cell membrane** of some **bacteria** that contains **enzymes** that control the osmotic stability of the **cell**.

Messenger ribonucleic acid (mRNA). A single-stranded **nucleic acid** that is the product of the **transcription** of a **deoxyribonucleic acid**-encoded structural **gene**. In **eukaryotes**, the complete mRNA travels from the **nucleus** to the rough **endoplasmic reticulum**, where **ribo-**

somes initiate its **translation** into a **polypeptide** chain. In **prokaryotes**, transcription occurs in the **cytoplasm**, where the mRNA is immediately accessible to clusters of ribosomes (**polysomes**) as soon as it is made. The translation process can thus begin before transcription is completed, a phenomenon referred to as cotranslation.

✔ Structural genes, from which mRNA is transcribed, are those that code for polypeptide chains, in contrast to regulatory genes and those genetic sequences that encode ribosomal ribonucleic acid or transfer ribonucleic acid.

Compare to **transfer ribonucleic acid**, **ribosomal ribonucleic acid**

Metabolism. The sum of all chemical reactions (e.g., **catabolism, anabolism, digestion**) carried out by an organism.

Meta-directing substituents. Chemical groups (e.g., NO_2, CF_3, COOH) that make an aromatic ring less susceptible than benzene to **electrophilic aromatic substitution** and direct the **electrophile** to the meta position *(Figure 59)*. Note that the meta position is not activated (i.e., able to more readily undergo electrophilic aromatic substitution), it is just deactivated *less* than the other ring positions. All meta-directors are "deactivating" (i.e., they make the ring less reactive than benzene). None of the meta-directors have an unshared **electron** pair on the **atom** that is directly bonded to the ring structure. These substituents carry a partial positive charge and are thus electron-withdrawing.

Compare to **ortho, para-directing substituents**

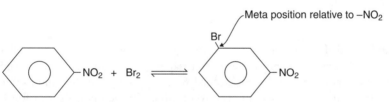

Figure 59. Meta-directing substituent

Metaphase. The "second" stage of **mitosis** in which the **microtubules** are organized in the **spindle apparatus** and the **chromosomes** are arranged on the equatorial plane of the spindle (i.e., in the center of the **cell**). The plane upon which the chromosomes appear to be lined up is called the metaphase plate. The end of metaphase is signalled by the division of **centromeres**, which results in the separation of the sister **chromatids** from one another. In **meiosis**:

- metaphase I is characterized by the alignment of the **homologous pairs** on the spindle apparatus. Each homologue is attached to a single microtubule that originates from one pole of the cell.
- metaphase II is similar to the mitotic metaphase in that the chromosomes, each consisting of a pair of sister chromatids, line up on the metaphase plate. The important difference is that because **crossing-over** occured during **prophase** I, the sister chromatids are no longer genetically identical to one another.

See also **anaphase, interphase, prophase, telophase**

Methyl group (—CH₃). A common organic substituent that is composed of a single sp^3-hybridized carbon **atom** bonded to three hydrogens. One **hybrid atomic orbital** is available for bonding.

Microfilaments. Actin and **myosin** fibers that help to maintain **cell** structure and permit cellular motility and **muscle contraction**. They are the smallest of the cytoskeletal **proteins**.

Compare to **intermediate filaments, microtubules**

Microorganism. A microscopic, single-celled organism (e.g., **bacteria, viruses**).

✔ There is controversy as to whether viruses are actually living organisms. However, most would agree that viruses can be classified as microbes because their relationships with humans often have general similarities to the interactions between bacteria or protozoans and humans.

Also called microbe

Microtubules. Hollow tubes composed of the **protein** tubulin. They are the structural components of **flagella**, **cilia**, and the mitotic and meiotic **spindle apparatus**, and also aid in intracellular transport. They are the largest of the cytoskeletal proteins.

Microvilli. Short, numerous extensions of the **cell membrane** that greatly increase the absorptive surface area of the **cell**. For example, they can be found on the **epithelium** of the **small intestine**.

✔ Microvilli are at the cellular level, while **intestinal villi** are at the histologic (i.e., **tissue**) level.

Midbrain. A portion of the **brain** that serves mainly to relay **nerve impulses** from one part of the brain to another.

Also called mesencephalon

Middle ear. The air-filled region of the ear that contains the ossicular system, which is a series of three small **bones**: the incus, malleus, and stapes. These bones conduct **sound** waves from the **tympanic membrane** to the **cochlea**. Most of the **energy** of the sound **waves** would normally be lost because the vibrations travel from air in the middle ear to **fluid** in the **inner ear**; however, the ossicular system acts as a lever to increase the **pressure** exerted on the cochlear fluid to compensate for the greater **inertia** of the fluid as compared to the air (this is called impedance matching).

Minerals. See **trace minerals**

Mirror equation. A formula that relates the object **distance** (o) and image distance (i) to the **focal length** (f) of a mirror:

$$\frac{1}{o} + \frac{1}{i} = \frac{1}{f}$$

✔ Notice that the mirror equation is identical to the **lens equation**.

✔ Recall that the focal length is positive for a **concave mirror** and negative for a **convex mirror**.

See also **lateral magnification**

Mitochondria. Membrane-bound, eukaryotic cell **organelles** that are the site of the **Krebs cycle** and **oxidative phosphorylation** and are the most important producers of **adenosine triphosphate** for the **cell** *(Figure 60)*.

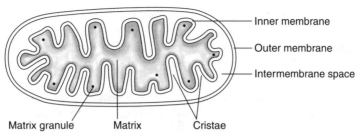

Figure 60. Mitochondrion

Mitosis. The replication and division of the **nucleus** of a eukaryotic **cell** that permits the reproduction of single-celled **eukaryotes** or the growth of multicellular organisms. The **chromosomes** of a single **somatic cell** are replicated and subsequently segregate to form two daughter **nuclei**, both of which contain a **diploid** set of chromosomes. Mitosis is usually followed by **cytokinesis**, which results in the formation of two diploid daughter cells. There are four major stages of mitosis: **prophase**, **metaphase**, **anaphase**, and **telophase** (see Appendix A, Figure 3).

> ✔ Dividing mitosis into four stages is for analysis only, because the entire process is seamlessly continuous. If you have trouble remembering the order of the stages, try the obvious acronym, PMAT.

Compare to **meiosis**

Molality (m). The number of **moles** of **solute** per kilogram of **solvent**. This measure of **concentration** does not change with **temperature**.

Compare to **molarity**

Molar heat capacity. The amount of **heat** required to raise the **temperature** of one **mole** of a substance by one degree (Kelvin or Celsius):

- Molar heat capacity at constant volume $= C_v$
- Molar heat capacity at constant **pressure** $= C_p$

Molarity (M). The number of **moles** of **solute** per liter of **solution**. This measure of **concentration** varies with **temperature**.

Compare to **molality**

Mole. The quantity of any substance that contains 6.02×10^{23} particles. This number is referred to as Avogadro's number and is symbolized N_A.

Molecular compound. A substance that is composed of discrete, individual **molecules**.

Compare to **ionic compound**

Molecular formula. The chemical formula of a **molecule** in a **molecular compound** that gives the exact number of **atoms** of each **element** in that single molecule.

Compare to **empirical formula**

Molecular orbital. A linear combination of **atomic orbitals** that involves an entire **molecule** through the delocalization of **electrons**.

Molecular spin quantum number. See **spin quantum number**

Molecular weight. The mass of one **mole** of a substance in grams. It is equal to the sum of the masses (in g/mol) of the **atoms** in one **molecule** of the substance.

Molecule. A combination of **atoms** (usually nonmetal **elements**) bound so strongly together that they act as a single particle. It is the smallest unit of a **molecular compound**.

Mole fraction (X). The number of **moles** of one component of a mixture divided by the total number of moles of all components in the mixture.

Momentum. A measure of the tendency of an object to maintain motion in a straight line, given by the equation:

$$p = mv$$

m = mass of the object
v = **velocity** of the object

A change in momentum (Δp) is called an **impulse**.

    ✔ Linear momentum is a **vector**.

Monocyte. A circulating **leukocyte** that is formed in the **bone marrow**. It is a precursor (i.e., a **cell** that gives rise to a more mature cell type via **mitosis**) of **macrophages**.

Monomer. A relatively small **molecule** (e.g., **amino acid, monosaccharide**) that can combine with identical or similar molecules to form a **polymer**. Monomers are often referred to as subunits.

Monosaccharide. A five- or six-carbon **carbohydrate**, or sugar **molecule** (e.g., **glucose**, ribose), that can combine with other monosaccharides to form **disaccharides** or **polysaccharides**. The cyclic form of monosaccharides are called cyclic **hemiacetals**. All of the common monosaccharides can exist as both α and β **anomers**.

Motor neuron. A general type of **neuron** that transmits **impulses** from the **central nervous system** to effector **organs**.

    Compare to **sensory neuron**

mRNA. See **messenger ribonucleic acid**

Mucosa. The interior lining of most hollow **organs** (e.g., **small intestine, stomach, trachea, vagina, uterus**). It consists of a layer of **epithelium**, an underlying loose **connective tissue** layer, and, in certain cases, a layer of **smooth muscle**. The lining is often referred to as a mucosal surface. In the digestive tract, projections of the mucosa into the lumen are called **intestinal villi**.

    ✔ Some hollow organs are not lined by mucosa; for example, **blood vessels** are lined by **intima**.

Muscle. See **cardiac muscle, skeletal muscle, smooth muscle**

Muscle cell. A **cell** that contains large amounts of **actin** and **myosin** arranged in such a way as to allow the cell to contract in synchronization with adjacent muscle cells.

✔ When discussing **skeletal muscle**, the term muscle cell is synonymous with **muscle fiber**.

Muscle contraction. In **skeletal muscle**, muscle contraction involves the shortening of a **sarcomere**, which occurs when calcium **ions** bind to **troponin**, allowing **myosin** heads (i.e., globular ends of the myosin **molecule**) to bind and slide along the **actin** filaments. This process requires the **hydrolysis** of **adenosine triphosphate**. As a result of muscle contraction, the Z-lines (i.e., the borders of each sarcomere) are pulled closer together and the **myofibril** is shortened.

Muscle fiber. In **skeletal muscle**, it is a single, cylindrical, multi-nucleated **muscle cell** formed by the end-to-end fusion of several muscle cells. In **cardiac muscle** fibers, adjacent muscle cells remain distinct and uninucleate. Several **myofibrils**, which run down the center of each muscle fiber, contract simultaneously to change the length of the fiber.

Muscle tone. Alternating groups of **muscle fibers** contract and relax to maintain a constant form and position.

Mutarotation. A slow, spontaneous change in optical rotation that leads to an equilibrium between the α and β **anomers** and the open-chain **conformations** of a **monosaccharide**.

Mutation, chromosomal. A stable, heritable change in the genetic material of an organism. Mutations are responsible for genetic variability; however, mutations in **somatic cells** have no effect on the **evolution** of the organism. Chromosomal mutations, which tend to become **recessive** traits if passed to the next generation, result from the following chromosomal events:
- Inversion (a sequence of **genes** on a **chromosome** is reversed)
- Translocation (a part of one chromosome attaches to another)
- Deletion (a part of a chromosome is missing)
- Duplication (a part of a chromosome is repeated)

Myelin sheath. A fatty material formed by **Schwann cells** that surrounds the **axons** of **motor neurons** in the **peripheral nervous system** and permits **saltatory conduction**.

Myofibrils. Long, parallel bunches of **actin** and **myosin microfilaments** that run through **muscle fibers**. Every myofibril is a chain of repeating units called **sarcomeres**, each of which is composed of an actin and myosin contractile assembly. It is the shortening and lengthening of myofibrils that permits **muscle contraction**.

Myosin. Thick **protein microfilaments** that each consist of a long rod with two globular heads at one end. Myosin is characteristically found in the **sarcomere**. It is not anchored at the Z-lines, but can form cross-bridges with adjacent **actin** filaments during **muscle contraction**.

N

Natural frequency. The particular **frequency** (f) at which an object vibrates when it is set in motion. The **period** (T) of an object undergoing **simple harmonic motion**, such as an oscillating spring, is dependent only on the mass and stiffness of the spring, not on the **amplitude** of vibration. Therefore, whenever a spring is set in motion, it will always have the same period and frequency (i.e., natural frequency) of **oscillation**.

> ✔ Recall that $T = \dfrac{1}{f}$.

See also **resonance, def. (1)**

Natural killer (NK) cells. Specialized **lymphocytes** that attack and kill cancerous **cells** or cells that have been infected by a **virus**. Although NK cells can be directed toward cells that are tagged by **antibodies** [a mechanism called antibody-dependent cell-mediated cytotoxicity (ADCC)], the activity of NK cells is generally part of a nonspecific **immune response**.

Natural selection. The Darwinian theory that the environment guides **evolution** by imposing conditions that select individuals with genetic traits that increase the likelihood of survival relative to other individuals in the same **population**. The traits do not arise out of need, but are simply the result of random, heritable chromosomal **mutations**.

> *Compare to* **artificial selection**

Negative feedback. See **feedback inhibition**

Nephron. The functional unit of the **kidney** that filters and selectively reabsorbs the constituents of **blood** to retain nutrients while excreting soluble waste products in the **urine** (see Appendix A, Figure 14).

Nernst equation. A formula that relates the **cell voltage** ($\mathscr{E}_{cell}$; **electromotive force**) to the **concentrations** of the chemical species taking part in the cell reaction:

$$\Delta\mathscr{E}_{cell} = \Delta\mathscr{E}^{\circ}_{cell} - (RT/n\mathscr{F})\ln Q$$

$\Delta\mathscr{E}^{\circ}_{cell}$ = the electromotive force when all substances are in their **standard states**
  R = universal **gas** constant
  T = absolute **temperature**
  n = number of **moles** of **electrons** transferred
  $\mathscr{F}$ = a **faraday** = 96,485 C/mol
  Q = reaction quotient for the net cell reaction

> ✔ The reaction quotient (Q) is calculated using the same equation that is used to calculate the **equilibrium constant**, except that the reaction does not have to be at its **equilibrium state** (i.e., $Q = K_{eq}$ only at equilibrium).

Nerve. A bundle of unmyelinated and myelinated **neurons** in the **peripheral nervous system**.

> *Compare to* **tract**

Nerve impulse. An **action potential** that is propagated along the membrane of a **neuron**.

Neural crest. A group of **cells** that arise from the **neural groove** during **neurulation**, just before the **neural tube** is formed. It eventually gives rise to a variety of nervous system structures (e.g., **adrenal medulla, myelin sheaths**). The development of the neural crest is unique to **vertebrates**.

Neural groove. A layer of **ectoderm** that invaginates and forms a groove during **neurulation**. The neural groove runs along the **notochord**.

Neural tube. A hollow tube that forms when the edges of the **neural groove** fuse during **neurulation**. It eventually gives rise to the **spinal cord** and the **brain**.

Neuroglia. See **glial cell**

Neuromuscular junction. A **synapse** between a **nerve** ending and a **muscle cell**.

Neuron. A **cell** that is highly differentiated and specialized for the **conduction** and transmission of electrical signals, such as **nerve impulses** (see Appendix A, Figure 8).

> *See also* **axon, dendrite, interneuron, motor neuron, myelin sheath, sensory neuron**

Neurotransmitter. A chemical substance that is released by the terminal portion of an **axon** and travels across the **synapse** to initiate an **action potential** in an adjacent **neuron, muscle,** or **gland cell**.

> *See also* **acetylcholine, noradrenaline**

Neurula. The **embryo** during **neurulation**.

Neurulation. The stage of **embryogenesis** in which the **neurula** is present. It begins when the **mesoderm** forms the **notochord** and the **ectoderm** forms the dorsal **nerve** chord. This stage is characteristic of **chordates**.

> *See also* **notochord, neural groove, neural crest, neural tube** (*in that order*)

Neutralization. A chemical reaction in which an **acid** reacts with a **base**. The reaction results in the formation of a **salt** and water.

Neutron. A particle contained in the **nucleus** of an **atom**. It is chargeless, but has a mass that is almost identical to that of a **proton**.

Neutrophil. A type of **leukocyte** that is involved in the inflammatory and nonspecific **immune response**. Neutrophils are large, numerous phagocytic **cells** that engulf **microorganisms** (e.g., **bacteria**), destroy them, and then die. They are rapid responders, but are short-lived.

Newton (N). A unit of **force** that accelerates a body with a mass of one kilogram at a rate of one meter per second squared:

$$1 \text{ N} = 1 \text{ kg} \cdot \text{m/s}^2$$

Newton's laws of motion.

- Newton's first law (law of inertia) states that an object remains in either a state of rest or motion with constant **velocity** unless it is acted on by an external **force**.
- Newton's second law of motion states that a net force (F) applied to a body or object gives rise to an acceleration (a) that is directly proportional to the force and inversely proportional to its mass (m). The direction of motion is in the direction of the force. In equation form, this law is stated as:

$$a \propto F/m \ or \ F = ma$$

- Newton's third law of motion is commonly stated as, "for every action, there is an equal and opposite reaction." This refers to the idea that when one object exerts a force on another object, the latter exerts an equal and opposite force on the former. For example, if you hit your hand against a desk, you exert a force on the desktop; however, the desktop exerts a force of equal magnitude back against your hand, resulting in pain. The concept of **normal force** is addressed by this law.

Nitrogenous base. A nitrogen-containing **molecule** that is a component of the **nucleic acid** subunit called a **nucleotide**. There are two classes of nitrogenous bases: **purines** and **pyrimidines**. In the **deoxyribonucleic acid** double helix, a purine on one strand undergoes **hydrogen bonding** with a pyrimidine on the complementary strand. A pair of nucleotides associated by such bonding are called a **base pair**.

Node. A point of maximal **destructive interference** where there is a complete absence of particle **displacement** for **mechanical waves**.

Nodes of Ranvier. Sites on the **plasma membrane** of a myelinated **neuron** where the **myelin sheath** is interrupted and the **axon** is in direct contact with the surrounding intercellular **fluid**. Because this is where most of the voltage-gated **ion** channels are localized, **action potentials** are propagated along the axon by leaping from one node to the next (**saltatory conduction**).

Nonpolar molecules. Molecules that do not have **dipole moments**. They are usually **hydrophobic** and can be dissolved in nonpolar organic **solvents**.

Noradrenaline. A chemical **neurotransmitter** released at most postganglionic **synapses** in the **sympathetic nervous system**. It also acts as a **hormone** that is produced by the **adrenal medulla** in response to sympathetic stimulation. A **neuron** that secretes noradrenaline is said to be adrenergic.

> *Also called* norepinephrine
> *Compare to* **acetylcholine**

Normal force (N; F$_N$). The upward contact **force** exerted against an object or body that exerts its **weight** against a surface. The normal force is perpendicular to the surface and essentially balances the force of **gravity** *(Figure 61)*.

> ✔ When talking about normal force, "normal" means perpendicular.

> See also **Newton's third law of motion**

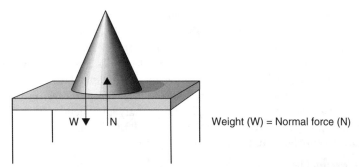

Figure 61. Normal force

Notochord. A rod of **mesoderm** that runs down the back of **chordate embryos**. It is eventually replaced by the vertebral column.

Nuclear binding energy. The **energy** that would be released if a **nucleus** was constructed from its individual **nucleons**.

Nuclear force. A nonelectrical, attractive **force** that acts at very short **distances** to bind the **nucleons** of an **atom** together.

Nuclear magnetic resonance (^{1}H NMR) spectroscopy. A method for determining a molecular structure by measuring the number and type of **protons** in a compound. It specifically provides information about the hydrogen and carbon **atoms**, which are details that the **infrared spectroscopy** does not pick up well. The technique is based on the absorption of radio **waves** by **nuclei** when they are placed into a particular **magnetic field**.

 ✔ A detailed explanation of ^{1}H NMR is beyond the scope of this book. However, an understanding of proton NMR spectroscopy is very important for the MCAT. You should be familiar with the concepts of nuclear magnetic moments, chemical shifts, **resonance**, shielding, equivalent and nonequivalent protons, and spin-spin coupling and splitting.

Nuclear membrane. The double membrane that encases the **nucleus** of a **cell**. The outer layer is often continuous with the **endoplasmic reticulum** of the cell.

 Also called nuclear envelope

Nuclear pore. A **protein** complex embedded in the **nuclear membrane**. It serves as a channel through which water-soluble **molecules** are transported between the **nucleus** and the **cytoplasm**; for example, **messenger ribonucleic acid** molecules are actively exported out of the nucleus.

Nuclear reaction. A change in the composition of the **nucleus** of an **atom**.

Nucleic acid. A polymeric strand of **nucleotides** joined by **phosphodiester bonds**. The two major types are **deoxyribonucleic acid**, which is usually found as two complementary nucleic acid strands in a double helix, and **ribonucleic acid**, which is typically single-stranded.

Nucleolus. A site in the **cell** nucleus where **ribosomal ribonucleic acid** synthesis takes place. It is a dark-staining area of the **nucleus**.

Nucleon. A **proton** or a **neutron**.

Nucleophile. A chemical species that is **electron**-rich and is thus attracted to positively-charged species. Most nucleophiles are **anions**; however, other **molecules** containing **atoms** with unshared **valence electrons** (e.g., H_2O, CH_3OH) also act as nucleophiles. As a rule, a stronger **base** is usually a stronger nucleophile. Nucleophiles can cause **elimination reactions** and **nucleophilic substitutions** when attacking an alkyl halide. The product formed depends on the structure of the alkyl halide, strength of the base, **temperature**, and nature of the **solvent**. In general, methyl halides (CH_3X) and primary alkyl halides (CH_3CH_2X) usually yield substitition products, tertiary alkyl halides [$(CH_3)_3CX$] tend to undergo elimination, and secondary alkyl halides [$(CH_3)_2CHX$] can go either way.

Compare to **electrophile**

Nucleophilic addition. An **addition reaction** in which a **nucleophile** attacks and binds to the carbon **atom** in a **carbonyl group**, resulting in an sp^3-hybridized carbon atom. The synthesis of cyanohydrin illustrates nucleophilic addition *(Figure 62)*.

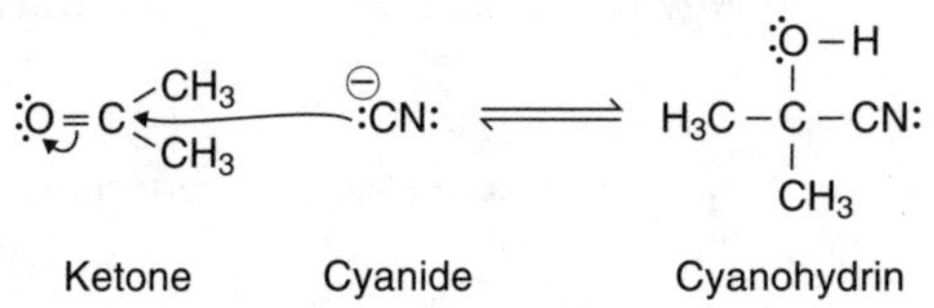

| Ketone | Cyanide | Cyanohydrin |

Figure 62. Nucleophilic addition

Nucleophilicity. A relative measure of the ability of a reagent to cause a **substitution reaction**.

Nucleophilic substitution. A **substitution reaction** in which a **nucleophile** attacks a positively-charged carbon **atom** and, in binding to it, displaces another nucleophile referred to as the leaving group. The most common leaving groups are halide **ions**, such as Cl^-, Br^-, or I^-. Halides are good leaving groups because they are **weak bases**. I is most easily displaced, followed by Br, then Cl. **Strong bases**, such as OH^-, are poor leaving groups. There are two major mechanisms of nucleophilic substitution:

- S_N2 reactions (substitution, nucleophilic, bimolecular). A strong nucleophile (Nu) collides with the "back side" of a tetrahedral (sp^3-hybridized) carbon atom of an alkyl halide (RX) and forms a new bond at the same time as the bond between the carbon and the leaving group is breaking. It is called a bimolecular reaction because the **activated complex** involves two species, Nu and RX. The result is an inversion of **configuration** [i.e., if the reactant has an (R) configuration, then the product will have an (S) configuration, and vice versa] *{Figure 63}*. The relative rates of reaction of the alkyl halides are determined by steric hindrance (i.e., as the number of **alkyl groups** increases, the rate of reaction decreases). As a result, methyl halides rapidly undergo S_N2 reactions, primary alkyl halides are slightly slower, and secondary alkyl halides are even slower. Tertiary alkyl halides do not undergo S_N2 reactions.

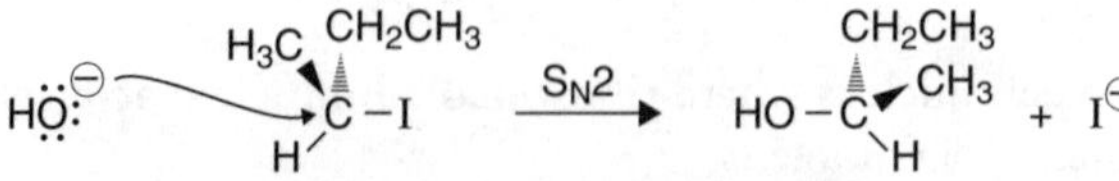

Figure 63. Nucleophilic substitution (S_N2 reaction)

- S_N1 solvolysis reactions (substitution, nucleophilic, unimolecular). (1) The alkyl halide is cleaved into the halide ion and a **carbocation** by a polar **solvent** (e.g., H_2O), (2) a nucleophile that is a weak base (e.g., H_2O) attacks the carbocation and forms a protonated **alcohol**, and (3) the protonated alcohol undergoes an acid-base reaction with the solvent to yield an alcohol *(Figure 64)*. The relative rates of reaction of the alkyl halides are largely determined by the stability of the carbocation. Because tertiary alkyl halides yield carbocations that are of lower **potential energy** than those of secondary alkyl halides, the former compounds undergo reaction much faster than the latter. Methyl halides and primary alkyl halides do not undergo S_N1 reactions. Unlike S_N2 reactions, the products of an S_N1 reaction involving a chiral **molecule** usually form a **racemic mixture**.

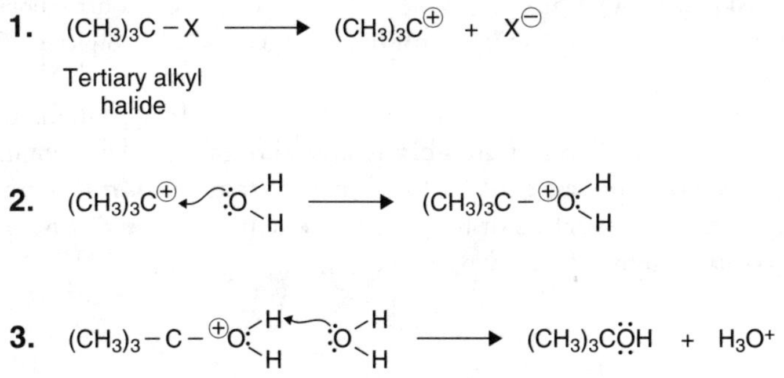

1. $(CH_3)_3C-X \longrightarrow (CH_3)_3C^{\oplus} + X^{\ominus}$

        Tertiary alkyl
          halide

2. $(CH_3)_3C^{\oplus} \; \ddot{O}\!\!<^H_H \longrightarrow (CH_3)_3C-^{\oplus}\ddot{O}\!\!<^H_H$

3. $(CH_3)_3-C-^{\oplus}\ddot{O}\!\!<^H_H \quad \ddot{O}\!\!<^H_H \longrightarrow (CH_3)_3C\ddot{O}H + H_3O^+$

Figure 64. Nucleophilic substitution (S_N1 reaction)

Nucleotide. A **monomer** of a **nucleic acid** that is composed of a five-carbon sugar [i.e., ribose in **ribonucleic acid (RNA)** and deoxyribose in **deoxyribonucleic acid (DNA)**], a **phosphate group**, and a **nitrogenous base** (either a **purine** or a **pyrimidine**) [*Figure 65* and Table 1]. The following "equations" can be used to distinguish a nucleoside from a nucleotide:

Nucleoside = nitrogenous base + sugar

Nucleotide = (nucleoside) + phosphate gr = (nitrogenous base + sugar) + phosphate gr

In DNA, nucleotides can be referred to as deoxyribonucleoside triphosphates (dNTP), and in RNA they are analogously called ribonucleoside triphosphates (NTP).

Be aware that nucleotides have many functions other than that of nucleic acid monomers. They can serve as **energy** carriers [e.g., **adenosine triphosphate (ATP)**], they can combine with other compounds to form **coenzymes** (e.g., coenzyme A), and they can act as chemical messengers [e.g., cyclic adenosine monophosphate (cAMP)].

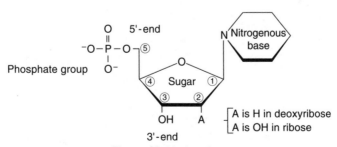

Figure 65. Nucleotide

Table 1. Common Nucleotides

NUCLEOTIDE	NUCLEOSIDE	NITROGENOUS BASE	ABBREVIATION
Adenosine triphosphate	Adenosine	Adenine	A
Guanosine triphosphate	Guanosine	Guanine	G
Cytidine triphosphate	Cytidine	Cytosine	C
Thymidine triphosphate	Thymidine	Thymine	T
Uridine triphosphate	Uridine	Uracil	U

✔ A nucleotide can refer to any nucleoside plus one or more phosphate groups. Only the names of the nucleoside triphosphates (NTPs) are indicated here and in Table 1 because they are the molecules that are added to the 3′-OH ends of growing nucleic acid chains. Other derivations are named accordingly [e.g., adenosine monophosphate (AMP), deoxyguanosine diphosphate (dGDP)].

Nucleus. (1) An atomic nucleus is the central core of the **atom** that contains **protons** and **neutrons**. (2) A cellular nucleus is a **membrane**-bound **organelle** that contains the **chromosomes** and the **deoxyribonucleic acid replication** and **transcription** machinery. It is only found in **eukaryotes**. (3) A nucleus in the nervous system is a cluster of **nerve cell** bodies in the **central nervous system**.

O

Obligate anaerobe. An organism that cannot live in the presence of oxygen. For its **energy** production, it uses an alternate final **electron** acceptor to carry out an **anaerobic respiration** process such as **fermentation**.

> *See also* **facultative anaerobe**
> *Compare to* **aerobe**

Octet rule. There is a maximum of eight **electrons** that can exist in the outermost **electron shell** of an **atom**.

> ✔ This rule only holds true for second row **elements**.

Ohm (Ω). The unit of **resistance** for which:

$$1 \ \Omega = 1 \ V/A$$

V = **volt**
A = **Ampere**

Ohm's law. The **current** flowing through a given conducting device in a **circuit** is directly proportional to the **potential difference** across the device and inversely proportional to the **resistance** that the device provides:

$$V = iR \quad \text{or} \quad i = \frac{V}{R}$$

V = the potential difference (in **volts**)
i = the current (in **amperes**)
R = the resistance (in **ohms**)

Oils. **Liquid** triacyl glycerols that contain mostly unsaturated **fatty acids**.

Oncotic pressure. The **osmotic pressure** that tends to pull **fluids** and **molecules** into capillaries. It is primarily caused by the large quantity of **albumin** in the **blood plasma**.

Oocyte. A **cell** that gives rise to an **ovum** by **meiosis**.

> *See also* **primary oocyte**

Opsonization. The facilitation of **phagocytosis** by the binding of **antibodies** or certain **complement** components to the surface of an **antigen**.

Optical activity. The property of **enantiomers** that refers to their ability to rotate plane-polarized light in a specific direction and to a specific degree of rotation.

Optical isomers. See **enantiomers**

Orbital. See **atomic orbital** and **hybrid orbital**

Orbital electron capture. A radioactive decay process in which the **nucleus** takes an **electron** from the K shell (the **electron shell** with the two 1s electrons) and then converts a **proton** to a **neutron**.

> *Also called* K capture

Order of reaction. The sum of the exponents in the experimentally determined **rate expression** for a given chemical reaction.

Organ. A collection of **tissues** that form a unique structural and functional unit in the body.

Organelle. A functional unit within a **cell**.

Organ of Corti. The neural apparatus of the **cochlea** responsible for the generation of **nerve impulses** in response to the vibration of the **basilar membrane**.

Ortho, para-directing substituents. Chemical groups that are **electron**-donating (e.g., $-NH_2$, $-OH$, **alkyl groups**), and thus make an aromatic ring structure more reactive than benzene. They direct **electrophiles** to the ortho and para positions *(Figure 66)*. Note that all o,p-directors, except the halogens (i.e., Cl, Br, I), are activating groups (i.e., cause the ring to be more susceptible to electrophilic attack).

> *Compare to* **meta-directing substituents**

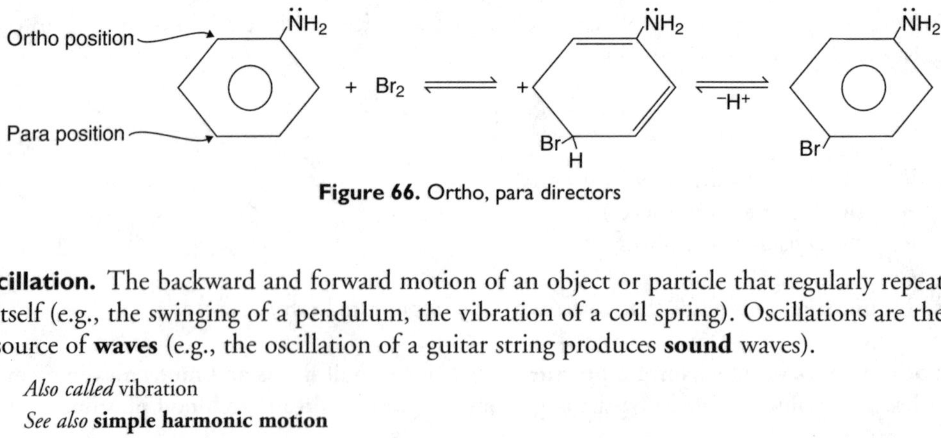

Figure 66. Ortho, para directors

Oscillation. The backward and forward motion of an object or particle that regularly repeats itself (e.g., the swinging of a pendulum, the vibration of a coil spring). Oscillations are the source of **waves** (e.g., the oscillation of a guitar string produces **sound** waves).

> *Also called* vibration
> *See also* **simple harmonic motion**

Osmosis. The **diffusion** of water across a semipermeable membrane (i.e., a barrier that allows water to flow, but prevents the flow of **solute**) from a **hypotonic solution** to a **hypertonic** solution.

Osmotic pressure. The amount of **pressure** needed to completely oppose **osmosis**. This is a measure of the **concentration** of **solute** in a **solution** (i.e., the greater the solute concentration, the higher the osmotic pressure).

Osteoblasts. **Bone**-forming **cells** that secrete **collagen** fibers upon which calcium **ions** are deposited. These cells eventually convert themselves into **osteocytes**.

Osteoclasts. **Cells** that remove **cartilage** scaffolding or mediate the resorption (i.e., destruction) of existing **bone**. This allows for the production, reshaping, or reconstruction of bone.

Osteocytes. **Cells** that are embedded within the **bone** matrix and maintain bone structure.

Oval window. The opening into the **inner ear**.

Ovary. The female gonad (reproductive **organ**) that produces female sex **hormones** and the female **gametes**.

Ovulation. The release of the secondary **oocyte** from the **ovary** into the **fallopian tube**.

Ovum. The female **gamete** that is produced from the **oocyte** during **meiosis**.

> *Also called* egg

Oxidation. The loss of **electrons** or, alternatively, the loss of hydrogen (H^+) in an organic or metabolic reaction. Oxidation always occurs simultaneously with **reduction** (i.e., one substance is oxidized while the other is reduced). Oxidation reactions are important **energy**-transfer reactions in metabolic processes.

Oxidation state. A value assigned to each **atom** or **ion** in a **redox reaction** that serves as a bookkeeping device for keeping track of the transfer of **electrons**. The oxidation state of a monoatomic ion is simply its charge; however, when assigning oxidation states to covalently-bonded atoms, the atom with the greatest **electronegativity** is given both electrons of the **shared pair**.

> *Also called* oxidation number

Oxidative phosphorylation. The **energy**-yielding process that occurs as follows:
- **Electrons** are extracted from fuel **molecules** (e.g., **glucose**) during the **oxidation** reactions of **glycolysis** and the **Krebs cycle**.
- The electrons are carried in the form of NADH or $FADH_2$, which are molecules that serve as **reducing agents** when they transfer their electrons into the **electron transport chain** at the inner surface of the mitochondrial membrane.
- The energy released as the electrons are passed down the chain of **cytochromes** drives **protons** into the mitochondrial intermembrane space and out into the **cytoplasm**.
- The accumulation of hydrogen ions (H^+) around the **mitochondria** generates a **protonmotive force**.
- The chemiosmotic production of **adenosine triphosphate** results from the **diffusion** of hydrogen through special enzymatic channels back into the mitochondrial matrix (internal region).

> ✔ Oxidative phosphorylation also occurs in some prokaryotic cells; however, because **prokaryotes** do not contain mitochondria, the reactions occur across the **cell membrane**.

> *See also* **chemiosmosis**

Oxidizing agent. A substance that takes **electrons** from other **atoms** (i.e., it oxidizes the atoms) and is itself reduced in the process.

> *Compare to* **reducing agent**

Oxygen debt. The unfulfilled oxygen requirement that builds up in **muscle fibers** during heavy exercise when **anaerobic respiration** (i.e., **glycolysis**) causes the accumulation of lactic acid, which is a product of **fermentation**. After exercise, the excess lactic acid must be removed by **oxidation** reactions that require oxygen as the final **electron** acceptor. In addition, oxygen stores that were depleted during exercise must be replenished. Therefore, the debt is "repaid" when aerobic respiration (e.g., **Krebs cycle**) processes resume.

✔ Lactic acid accumulation is responsible for muscle fatigue.

Oxytocin. A female **hormone** that causes the contraction of certain **smooth muscles** in the **uterus** and stimulates the mammary **glands** to release milk. It is synthesized by the **hypothalamus** and released by the posterior **pituitary gland**.

P

Paired electrons. Two **electrons** that occupy the same **atomic orbital**, but have opposite directions of spin. The only **quantum number** that differentiates the two electrons is the **spin quantum number** (m_s).

✔ Paired electrons are not the same as a **shared pair** of electrons that exists in a **covalent bond**.

Palate. The **tissue** that seals off the nasal cavity when swallowing is initiated.

Pancreas. A small **gland** that has both **exocrine** and **endocrine** functions.
- Exocrine functions include the production of a large number of digestive **enzymes** that are secreted into the **duodenum**.
- Endocrine functions include the production of **insulin** and **glucagon** by **cells** in the **islets of Langerhans**

Parallel circuit. A connection of **circuit** elements that have two common points (i.e., the **current** splits into separate branches and flows across each **element** with the same voltage). However, the currents in each branch are not equal. The total current (i) is equal to the sum of the currents in each path *(Figure 67)*. For a circuit with *n* **resistors**, the net **resistance**, which is less than that of each single resistor, is given by the following equation derived from **Ohm's law**:

$$\frac{1}{R} = \frac{1}{R_1} + \frac{1}{R_2} + \dots + \frac{1}{R_n}$$

R = resistance

✔ A circuit element could be a **capacitor** or a resistor.

Compare to **series circuit**

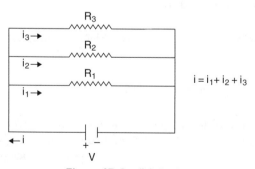

Figure 67. Parallel circuit

Paramagnetism. A property of materials whose individual **atoms** have at least one unpaired **electron**. These materials are attracted to external **magnetic fields**, but lose their magnetism when removed from the field. This is a stronger magnetism than **diamagnetism**, but is weaker than **ferromagnetism**.

Parasympathetic nervous system. The branch of the **autonomic nervous system** that is comprised of **efferent** nervous system pathways that maintain the body in a normal state and stimulate resting activities (e.g., **digestion**) that are antagonistic to sympathetically-stimulated activities. **Acetylcholine** is the major parasympathetic **neurotransmitter**. The **ganglia** of parasympathetic **nerves** are near or in the target **organs**.

> *Compare to* **sympathetic nervous system**

Parathyroid hormone. A **hormone** produced by the parathyroid **gland** that counteracts the effects of **calcitonin** by increasing the levels of calcium **ion** in the **blood plasma**. It stimulates **bone** resorption and calcium reabsorption in the **kidneys**.

Parietal cell. A type of **exocrine gland cell** in the gastric **mucosa** that secretes hydrochloric acid [$HCl_{(aq)}$] into the **stomach**. Although the acid has limited direct digestive action, it serves three major functions:

1.   Catalyzes the conversion of pepsinogen into the **protein**-hydrolyzing **enzyme pepsin**
2.   Causes the unfolding of **connective tissue** proteins
3.   Creates an environment that is quite unwelcoming to most potential pathogenic organisms

> ✔ Acidophiles (acid lovers) are a type of **bacteria** that thrive under acidic conditions; however, the stomach **pH** is approximately 0.8, which is low enough to kill most **microorganisms**.

Partial pressure. In a mixture of **gases**, it is the **pressure** that a single gas would exert if it alone filled the entire volume occupied by the mixture.

> *See also* **Dalton's law**

Pascal's law. An external **pressure** applied to an enclosed **fluid** is transmitted uniformly throughout the volume of the **liquid**.

> ✔ To visualize this law, think of the effects on the contents of a tube of toothpaste when it is squeezed.

Passive transport. See **facilitated diffusion**

Pauli's exclusion principle. No two **electrons** in the same **atom** can have the same four **quantum numbers**.

Pectin. A branched **polysaccharide** (e.g., amylopectin).

Pedigree. A diagram that explains the phenotypic appearance of genetic traits in a **family**. By constructing a pedigree, it is possible to determine the nature of a given heritable trait (e.g., autosomal recessive, X-linked). Common features of pedigrees include the following.

•   Males are typically shown as squares and females are shown as circles.
•   Horizontal lines indicate marriage.
•   Filled (solid) symbols indicate an individual who demonstrates the trait.
•   Roman numerals alongside the diagram represent the generations.

Figure 68 shows a pedigree for hemophilia (mutation in clotting factor VIII), which is an X-linked recessive trait. Males who inherit an X **chromosome** with the mutant **allele** will develop the disease. Females can pass on the trait without demonstrating the mutant **phenotype** if they are carriers [i.e., have one X chromosome carrying the normal (wild-type) allele while the other X chromosome carries the mutant allele].

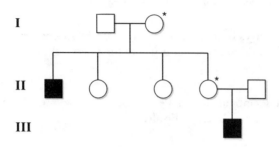

* These females must be carriers
Figure 68. Pedigree

Penile erection. A stiffening of the **penis** that occurs when parasympathetic stimulation causes dilation of small **blood vessels** in the penis and constriction of efferent venous tracts.

Penis. The external male genital **organ**.

Pepsin. A **stomach protease** that catalyzes the **hydrolysis** of **proteins** between particular **amino acids**. It is formed by the cleavage of pepsinogen, which is catalyzed by **acid**.

Peptide bond. The linkage between adjacent **amino acids** in **polypeptides**. It is an **amide** link between the amino group of one amino acid and the **carboxyl group** of another *(Figure 69)*. This linkage has a partial double-bond character (pseudo-sp^2-hybridization) and does not permit much rotation.

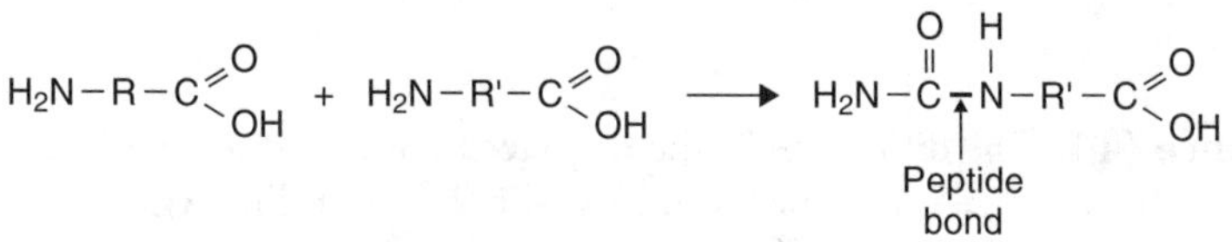

$$H_2N-R-C\underset{OH}{\overset{O}{\lessgtr}} \ + \ H_2N-R'-C\underset{OH}{\overset{O}{\lessgtr}} \longrightarrow H_2N-\underset{\underset{\text{Peptide}}{\uparrow}}{C}\overset{\overset{O \ \ H}{\parallel \ \ |}}{-}N-R'-C\underset{OH}{\overset{O}{\lessgtr}}$$

Peptide
bond

Figure 69. Peptide bond

Percent composition. To determine the percent composition of a **solution**, divide the amount of **solute** by the total amount of solution and multiply by 100.

Percent mass. The mass of one component of a mixture divided by the total mass of the mixture, multiplied by 100.

Period. (1) The time required for one **wavelength** to pass a given point in space. In a more general sense, it is the time in which an object or particle completes a single **oscillation** cycle. A period (T) is equal to the inverse of the **frequency** of a **wave** (T $\propto \frac{1}{f}$). (2) A horizontal row of the periodic table. Each of the seven rows corresponds to a **principle quantum number**.

Peripheral nervous system. The network of all **nerve** pathways outside of the **central nervous system** (see Appendix A, Figure 7).

> *See also* **autonomic nervous system, somatic nervous system**

Peristalsis. Rhythmic **waves** of **muscle contraction** in the **smooth muscle** that run the length of a tube or duct. For example, peristalsis moves food down the **esophagus** and through the **small intestine**.

Peroxisome. A single-membrane **organelle** that contains **enzymes** that metabolize hydrogen peroxide or convert **carbohydrates** to **lipids**.

pH. A measure of the relative hydrogen **ion concentrations** in **solutions** using a scale that ranges from 0–14. The pH of a solution is defined by the following equation:

$$pH = -\log[H_3O^+]$$

- A neutral solution, one in which the $[H_3O^+] = [OH^-]$, always has $[H_3O^+] = 1 \times 10^{-7}$. If you plug this into the pH equation, you will find that pH = 7.
- Acidic solutions are characterized by $[H_3O^+] > [OH^-]$ and pH < 7.
- Basic solutions are characterized by $[H_3O^+] < [OH^-]$ and pH > 7.

> *See also* **acid, base, Henderson-Hasselbach equation**

Phagocytosis. A form of **endocytosis** by which large, **solid** matter is surrounded and engulfed by the **plasma membrane** of a **cell**. The cell ingests the material and encloses it within the internal vesicle. This is the method by which **macrophages** engulf substances such as foreign cells and **viruses**.

> *Compare to* **exocytosis, pinocytosis**

Pharynx. A tubular path that leads from the mouth to the openings of the **esophagus** and **trachea**.

Phase difference (Φ). The difference in the **displacement** and direction of a particle due to the interaction (i.e., **interference**) between two **waves**. For dealing with waves of the same **frequency**, the phase difference is often indicated in terms of the symbol π ($2\pi = \lambda$, where λ is the **wavelength**). Two waves that undergo complete **constructive interference** are said to be in phase, meaning that $\Phi = 2\pi$. Because the phase difference equals one whole wavelength, the crests and troughs of the two waves coincide. Two waves that undergo complete **destructive interference** are said to be out of phase, meaning that $\Phi = n\pi$, where n = 1, 3, 5, and so on. In this case, a trough of one wave coincides with a crest of the other wave; thus, the waves cancel each other out.

> ✔ The particle referred to when discussing wave motion is a particle of the medium through which the wave is traveling. A **mechanical wave** itself is not composed of particles.

Phenol. A benzene ring lacking one hydrogen **atom** that acts as a substituent of another **molecule**. Its reactivity is due to the acidic **hydroxyl group** hydrogen. Under basic conditions, the acidic hydroxyl group hydrogen can be abstracted to form a relatively stable phenoxide **ion** (Ar-O⁻), which is a **resonance**-stabilized structure. Phenol undergoes **hydrogen bonding** and is a powerful **ortho, para-director**.

Phenotype. The visible expression of the **genotype** that may reflect the effect of environmental influences. A phenotype can refer to a specific trait or to the entire organism. The visible characteristics of an individual are often the result of the genotype at a number of genetic loci and can be referred to as multifactorial traits. For example, a phenomenon called "epistasis" is the interaction between the products of two genes in which one gene modifies the phenotypic expression of the other. Therefore, a knowledge of the allelic composition at a single **locus** will not always be an accurate predictor of the phenotypic result.

Phenyl group. A benzene ring that acts as a substituent of another **molecule**.

Phosphate group (PO_4; P_i). A chemical group commonly found in high-**energy** bonds [e.g., **adenosine triphosphate (ATP)**, **phosphodiester bonds**]. Phosphorylation is the reaction by which these bonds form; likewise, a phosphorylated compound is one that contains a phosphate group. The high-energy bond is often notated as a small, wavy line (e.g., ADP ∼ P_i is the same as ATP).

Phosphodiester bond. The **covalent bond** that forms between the 5′-end (a **phosphate group**) of one **nucleotide** and the 3′-end (a **hydroxyl group**) of an adjacent nucleotide to form the backbone of a **nucleic acid** chain.

Phospholipids. A class of **lipids** that contain phosphorylated **alcohols** attached to a **glycerol** backbone in place of one or more **fatty acid** chains. Because the **phosphate group** is **hydrophilic** and the fatty acid chains are **hydrophobic**, a phospholipid **molecule** is amphipathic, meaning it is soluble in both aqueous and organic **solvents**. This property is the basis of the formation of **lipid bilayers** in all biological membranes and the reason why detergents can solubilize **oils** in water.

See also **plasma membrane**

Photon. A quantum (discrete packet) of **electromagnetic radiation**. Although the idea that electromagnetic radiation travels as tiny particles of **energy** seems to be in direct opposition to the idea that light travels as a **wave**, it has been concluded that electromagnetic waves have both particle and wave properties. The concept of the photon is conveniently used when discussing the relationship between energy and the quantized atomic energy levels of an **atom**. The energy of a single photon is given by the equation:

$$E = hf$$

h = Planck's constant (h = 6.626×10^{-34} J · s)

f = the **frequency** of the wave

See also **absorption spectrum**

Photoreceptor. A specialized **cell** in the **retina** that sends a **nerve impulse** to the **brain** when stimulated by a particular **wavelength** of light that corresponds to the specificity of the given photoreceptor.

See also **cones, rods**

Pi (π) bond. An intramolecular bond formed by the sideways overlapping of the "p" **atomic orbitals** of different **atoms** that occurs where the **electron** density is above and below the axis of the two atoms *(Figure 70)*. The electrons in pi bonds are responsible for the rigidity of double bonds and are more reactive than **sigma bonds**.

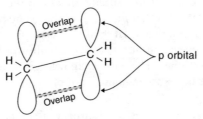

Figure 70. Pi bond

Pigment. Any **molecule** that is capable of absorbing light. The specific **wavelengths** that are absorbed by a given pigment depend on the availability of atomic **energy** levels to which light-capturing **electrons** can be boosted.

See also **absorption spectrum**

Pinna. The visible, outer, cupped portion of the **external ear** that helps to direct **sound waves** into the **auditory canal**.

Also called auricle

Pinocytosis. A form of **endocytosis** in which the **plasma membrane** invaginates and takes-up **liquid** droplets.

Compare to **phagocytosis**

Pitch. The quality of a **sound** that refers to whether it is high, like an air raid siren, or low, like a tuba. The pitch is determined by the **frequency** of the sound **wave**; the higher the frequency, the higher the pitch.

   ✔ In terms of the threshold of human hearing, the normal range of audible frequencies of sound is approximately 20–20,000 Hz.

Pituitary gland. A major **endocrine gland** that is attached to the **hypothalamus**, which controls its secretions. It hangs down from the base of the **brain** and consists of two lobes, the anterior and posterior.

- Anterior pituitary. Small **blood vessels** permit the transport of special releasing factors from the hypothalamus to the anterior lobe. The particular factor that is released determines which of the following **hormones** is secreted: **growth hormone, thyroid-stimulating hormone, luteinizing hormone, follicle-stimulating hormone, adrenocorticotropic hormone, prolactin**, or melanocyte-stimulating hormone.
- Posterior pituitary. The hypothalamus directs the secretions of the posterior lobe via direct neural connections. Both **antidiuretic hormone** and **oxytocin** are produced in the hypothalamus and are transferred to the pituitary, which releases them into the blood.

pK. A convenient way to express the **acidity constant** or **basicity constant**. It is calculated using the following equation:

$$pK = -\log K$$

See also **Henderson-Hasselbach equation, pH**

Placenta. A network of **blood vessels** that forms from the **chorion** and the **endometrium** during pregnancy. It mediates the **diffusion** of nutrients from the mother to the **embryo** (and later, the **fetus**) and the diffusion of waste from the embryo back into the mother.

Plasma. See **blood plasma**

Plasma cell. A mature **B lymphocyte** that has undergone complete **differentiation** and is specialized to produce **antibodies** of a particular binding specificity.

Plasma membrane. The **fluid** assembly of **lipids, carbohydrates,** and **proteins** that surrounds all living **cells** and mediates their interactions with the surrounding environment. The fluid mosaic model is commonly used to portray the membrane as a dynamic collection of **molecules** whose individual locations in the membrane are not entirely fixed. The basic foundation of the membrane is the **lipid bilayer**, which is a sheet composed of two parallel layers of **phospholipid** molecules *(Figure 71)*. The **hydrophobic fatty acid** tails of the two layers interact at the inner region of the membrane, while the **hydrophilic** ends project outward into the **cytoplasm** or the extracellular fluid. The fluidity of this structure is effected by the presence of **cholesterol** molecules that are interspersed among the phospholipids. While **nonpolar molecules** can pass across the membrane by **diffusion**, the hydrophobic internal aspect of the membrane is impermeable to water-soluble molecules (e.g., sugars, proteins, **ions**); however, these molecules are able to pass through the membrane due to the presence of transmembrane proteins (or integral proteins), which act as receptors, carriers, channels, and pumps. They not only regulate the uptake and exchange of ions and nutrients by mecha-

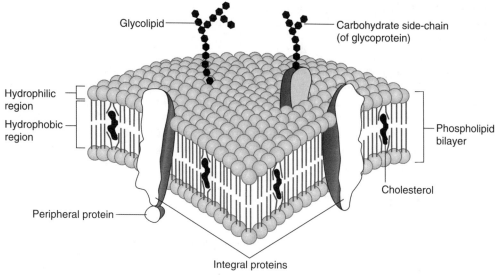

Figure 71. Plasma membrane

nisms such as **active transport** and **facilitated diffusion**, but also initiate the cellular response to incoming **hormones** and **cytokines**. Larger molecules, possibly even other cells, are taken-up by **endocytosis**. Additional membrane-bound proteins, glycoproteins, and glycolipids mediate various aspects of cell-to-cell communication.

    Also called cell membrane, plasmalemma

Platelets. Cellular fragments that regulate **blood** clotting (i.e., the control of bleeding). They are formed from precursors called megakaryocytes that are produced from **stem cells** in the **bone marrow**.

Pleural membrane. The thin, smooth membrane that covers each **lung**.

Polar bodies. Haploid by-products of female **meiosis** (i.e., **gamete** production) that have no apparent function.

Polarimeter. An instrument used to measure the rotation of polarized light that is caused by an **optical isomer**.

Polar molecule. A **molecule** that is made up of **elements** of different **electronegativities** and has slightly positively and negatively charged ends. Polar molecules are **hydrophilic** because they can form **hydrogen bonds** with water molecules.

    Compare to **nonpolar molecule**

Polyclonal response. An **immune response** in which a single **antigen** elicits the production of many different **antibodies**.

Polymer. A relatively large **molecule** composed of a series or chain of repeating subunits called **monomers**. For example, a **nucleic acid** is a linear polymer composed of **nucleotide** monomers.

Polymerization. The process by which **monomers** join to form a **polymer**. Biological polymers (e.g., **proteins, polysaccharides**) are usually formed by means of **condensation reactions**.

Polypeptide. A **polymer** of **amino acids** created by **condensation reactions** that result in the formation of **peptide bonds**. The particular sequence of amino acids is dictated during the **translation** of a **messenger ribonucleic acid molecule** by **ribosomes**. A polypeptide is often considered to be a **protein**; however, in many cases, individual polypeptides do not have a function of their own. Rather, the functional protein consists of multiple, interacting polypeptide chains. Whereas it used to be said, "one **gene**, one **enzyme**," the saying now goes, "one gene, one polypeptide."

Polysaccharide. A **polymer** containing multiple, repeating **monosaccharides** (e.g., **glycogen, starch**, cellulose).

Polysome. A cluster of **ribosomes** found in the **cytoplasm** of **bacteria**.

    Also called polyribosome

Pons. A component of the **brain stem** that mainly serves relay functions.

Population. A group of individuals from the same species that occupy the same place at the same time. Population growth can be determined using the following equation:

$$R = (B-D) \cdot \left[\frac{(C-N)}{C} \right] \cdot N$$

    B = births
    D = deaths
    N = number of individuals
    C = carrying capacity of the habitat

Posterior pituitary gland. See **pituitary gland**

Potential difference. A measure (a **scalar**) of the **work** done by an external **force** in moving a unit electric charge from point a to point b; for example, the work done by an **electric field** in moving a test charge from a higher **electric potential** to a lower potential. For a uniform electric field (E) with a distance d between points a and b, the potential difference is given as:

$$V = Ed$$

    ✔ The units of V are in **volts**.

Potential energy. The **energy** of an object or particle due to its position or **configuration**. This energy can be harnessed by converting it to another form. The magnitude of the potential energy of an object or particle is independent of the path taken to reach its position.

    Compare to **kinetic energy**

Power. (1) The rate at which **work** is done (a **scalar**), as given by:

$$P = \frac{W}{t} = \frac{(Fd)}{t} = Fv$$

    W = work
    t = time
    F = **force**
    d = **distance**
    v = **velocity**

The unit is the watt (W), where $1\ W = 1$ J/s. (2) Electric power is the rate of work performed by the **energy** that is lost as a result of a **current** flowing through a **resistor**. The magnitude of the power is given as:

$$P = Vi$$

    V = voltage
    i = current

(3) The power of a lens (P) is the reciprocal of the **focal length** (f) of a lens: $P = \frac{1}{f}$. The unit is the dioptre (D), which is equal to an inverse meter (m^{-1}).

Precipitation. The process by which **solid** particles come out of **solution** and settle to the bottom of the reaction flask. This occurs if a **solute** is added to a **saturated solution** or if the products of a reaction are insoluble in the **solvent**.

Pressure (P). The **force** applied per unit area. When the force is perpendicular to the surface, the following equation can be used:

$$P = \frac{F}{A}$$

F = force
A = area

The common units are the pascal (Pa), where 1 Pa = 1 N/m^2, and the atmosphere (atm), which is equal to 1.01325×10^5 Pa. To calculate how the pressure in a **fluid** varies with depth, the following equation is used:

$$P = \rho gh$$

ρ = **density** of the fluid
g = **acceleration** due to **gravity**
h = depth below the surface of the **liquid**

Primary oocyte. A **diploid cell** that is in the process of forming a female **gamete**, but has been arrested at **prophase** I of **meiosis** (see Appendix A, Figure 5). When **ovulation** occurs, the meiotic cycle proceeds and the **ovum** is produced.

Primordial follicle. The combination of a **primary oocyte** and **follicular cells** that reside in the **ovary**.

Principal quantum number (n). The component of an **electron configuration** that describes the general size and **energy** of an **atomic orbital**.

Also called atomic energy level

Progesterone. A **steroid hormone** secreted by the **corpus luteum** in females that mediates the completion of the thickening of the **endometrium** in preparation for **fertilization**. It also maintains the **uterus** during pregnancy.

Projectile motion. The parabolic path of an object that is projected into the air at a given angle and with a given initial **velocity**. The velocity and **displacement** of the object are both **vectors** and can be calculated as separate vertical (v_y, y) and horizontal (v_x, x) components using the equations in Table 2. In these equations, if we assume that y is positive for upward motion, then $g = -10$ m/s^2. The relationships shown in these equations only strictly apply when the projectile is close enough to the earth so that g is constant.

Table 2. Calculation of Velocity and Displacement

HORIZONTAL	VERTICAL
$v_x = v_{xo}$	$v_y = v_{yo} + gt$
$x = v_{xo}t$	$v_y^2 = v_{yo}^2 + 2gy$
$v_{xo} = v_o\cos\theta$	$y = v_{yo}t + \frac{1}{2}gt^2$
	$v_{yo} = v_o\sin\theta$

g = acceleration due to gravity; t = time; v = velocity; x = horizontal displacement; y = vertical displacement.

Prokaryote. A single-celled organism that lacks a **nucleus** and other membrane-bound **organelles**. **Bacteria** are the only prokaryotes in existence. Prokaryotic **cells** are considered to be more primitive than eukaryotic cells, which apparently evolved from early prokaryotes.

> *Compare to* **eukaryote** (see Appendix A, Table 1)

Prolactin. A **hormone** that stimulates breast milk production in females. It is secreted by the **anterior pituitary gland**.

Prophage. The latent stage of a phage, which is located in a **lysogenic cell**. During this stage, the **nucleic acid** strand of a **virus** is incorporated into the bacterial **chromosome**, and can thus be passed on to the bacterial progeny. The virus remains latent (inactive) until some future time when it may initiate cell **lysis**.

Prophase. The first stage of **mitosis** in which the **chromosomes** become fully condensed (i.e., coiled into compact rods). The **nuclear membrane** breaks down and the **spindle apparatus** begins to form. In **meiosis**, prophase I is characterized by the **condensation** of the chromosomes and subsequent **synapsis** (i.e., pairing of the **homologous pairs**). Prophase II is essentially the same as the mitotic prophase.

> *See also* **anaphase, interphase, metaphase, telophase**

Proprioceptors. Sensory **nerve** endings that detect body position or movement.

Prostate gland. A male **gland** that contributes some **fluids** to the **semen**.

Prosthetic group. An organic, **nonpolar molecule** that is tightly associated with an **enzyme** and serves as a **cofactor**. Prosthetic groups are often metal **ions** used to bind **substrates**.

> *Compare to* **coenzyme**

Protease. Any **enzyme** that breaks up **proteins** into **amino acids** by cleaving **peptide bonds**.

> *Also called* endopeptidase

Protein. A macromolecule that is composed of one or more **polypeptide** chains and has a structural or enzymatic function. Proteins can be generally classified into one of three groups:

- Fibrous proteins (e.g., **collagen**) are relatively insoluble and have structural purposes.
- Globular proteins (e.g., **hemoglobin**) are water soluble and have biological functions.
- Conjugated proteins (e.g., glycoprotein) are bound to nonprotein organic moieties.

The structure of a protein can be defined in terms of four levels of hierarchy:

- Primary structure. This structure refers to the sequence of **amino acids** in each polypeptide chain of which the protein is composed.
- Secondary structure. This refers to the pattern of amino acid interactions due to **hydrogen bonding** that exists between amino acid residues in a particular region in each polypeptide chain. There are two major classes of secondary structure. The α-helix is stabilized by hydrogen bonding between the **carbonyl group** of one residue and the N-H group of another residue, four away from the first residue. This forms a helical (i.e., coiled) structure. In the β-pleated sheet, the hydrogen bonds are formed between amino acid residues that are far apart on the polypeptide chain. In multimeric proteins, similar bonding is possible between residues on different polypeptides.

- Tertiary structure. This refers to the three-dimensional arrangement of a polypeptide that results from the interaction of the different regions of 2° structure in the chain. In extracellular proteins (i.e., those that are secreted into the **extracellular matrix**), this structure is often maintained by disulfide bonds that form between the —SH (sulfide) groups of neighboring cysteine residues. The formation of 3° structure is often referred to as folding. The tertiary structure is the highest level of structural organization for monomeric proteins (i.e., proteins that consist of only one polypeptide chain).

- Quaternary structure. This refers to the manner in which the subunits of a multimeric protein (i.e., a protein composed of more than one polypeptide chain) interact. It can consist of **hydrophobic** interactions, **ionic bonds**, disulfide bonds (in secreted proteins), and hydrogen bonding.

Although the definition of a protein domain is ambiguous, it usually refers to a specific 50–200 amino acid sequence that has a distinguishable and independent tertiary structure. Proteins in their physiologically stable **conformation** are said to be in their native state.

> *See also* **denaturation**

Proton. A subatomic particle with a positive charge that is contained in the **nucleus** of an **atom**. The mass of a single proton is equal to the mass of a **neutron** (i.e., approximately 1800 times the mass of an **electron**); however, the charge on the proton is equal and opposite to the charge of the electron.

> ✔ A hydrogen **ion** (H^+) is simply a single proton.

Protonmotive force. The **force** exerted as a result of the electrochemical **proton** gradient that arises when the **energy** derived from the **electron transport chain** is used to pump protons (H^+) out of the mitochondrial matrix into the intermembrane space and the **cytoplasm**. This force drives the protons back into the matrix through specialized **protein** channels that comprise a large **enzyme** complex called **adenosine triphosphate (ATP)** synthetase, which synthesizes ATP by harnessing the energy that is released as the protons flow down the electrochemical gradient.

> ✔ A gradient can be thought of as a slope that determines the direction of a chemical's flow. In the case of this electrochemical diffusion gradient, there is a **pH** gradient and a voltage gradient, both of which result from the outflow of H^+ from the mitochondrial matrix. The pH gradient exists because there is a higher concentration of H^+ in the cytosol than in the mitochondrial matrix, and the voltage gradient arises as a result of the net flow of positive charge out of the matrix.

> *See also* **chemiosmosis, oxidative phosphorylation**

Proximal convoluted tubule. The portion of the **nephron** where reabsorption first occurs. **Amino acids**, sugars (e.g., **glucose**), and other organic compounds are almost completely reabsorbed by **active transport** mechanisms. **Ions** (e.g., sodium, potassium, bicarbonate, chloride) are also largely reabsorbed in the proximal tubule. However, the osmolarity of the tubular **fluid** remains fairly constant because the **diffusion** of water out of the lumen, which is due to the H_2O permeability of the tubular membrane, is proportional to the rate of sodium reabsorption. The proximal tubule also actively secretes toxins, drugs, and certain metabolic end products into the tubular fluid. The membrane is relatively impermeable to **urea**.

Pulmonary circulation. The network of **blood vessels** that supplies blood to the **lungs**.

> *Compare to* **systemic circulation**

Pulmonary valve. A flap of **tissue** that separates the pulmonary **artery** and the right **ventricle**.

Also called pulmonic valve

Punnett square. A diagrammatical method for determining all possible **genotypes** and **phenotypes** of the progeny that may arise from the mating of two individuals of known genotypes. For example, the mating of two brown-eyed individuals who are both **heterozygous** for eye color is shown in *Figure 72* (B is the dominant brown **allele**, and b is the recessive blue allele). The resulting progeny shows a one-quarter probability of being **homozygous** dominant (brown-eyed), one-half probability of being heterozygous (brown-eyed), and one-quarter probability of being homozygous recessive (blue-eyed).

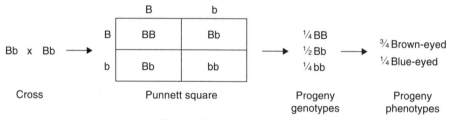

Figure 72. Punnett square

Pupil. The opening in the eyeball that allows light to enter. Its size is altered by the **iris** according to the amount of light entering.

Purine. A type of **nitrogenous base** that has a two-ring structure. The purines that are normally found in both **deoxyribonucleic acid** and **ribonucleic acid** are guanine and adenine.

Compare to **pyrimidine**

Purkinje fibers. Cardiac **tissue** that conducts a **depolarization** over the surface of the **ventricles** during **systole**.

Pyloric sphincter. A muscular constriction site that separates the **stomach** and the **duodenum**.

Pyrimidine. A type of **nitrogenous base** that has a single-ring structure. The pyrimidines normally found in **deoxyribonucleic acid** are thymine and cytosine. The pyrimidines normally found in **ribonucleic acid** are uracil and cytosine.

Compare to **purine**

Quantum. A discrete unit of definite quantity. At atomic and subatomic levels, **energy** is emitted and absorbed in quanta called **photons**.

See also **quantum number**

Quantum number. A value that describes some aspect of a physical or chemical property of a substance and is restricted to discrete (noncontinuous) integers. The most relevant example pertains to the use of quantum numbers to describe the **electron configuration** of an **atom**.

See also **angular momentum quantum number, magnetic quantum number, principal quantum number, spin quantum number**

Quaternary ammonium salt. An ammonium salt that has four **alkyl** or **aryl groups** bonded to nitrogen. The nitrogen thus forms part of a **cation** (i.e., $R_4N^+ \ X^-$). Quaternary ammonium salts with long hydrocarbon chains can act as detergents or phase-transfer agents that carry inorganic **ions** into organic (**hydrophobic**) **solvents**. This permits the occurrence of chemical reactions that would otherwise not easily proceed because the reagents are soluble in solvents of differing polarities.

R

Racemic mixture. An equimolar mixture of a pair of **enantiomers**. The mixture has no **optical activity**.

Radiation. (1) The transfer of **heat** by **electromagnetic (EM) waves**. This method of heat transfer differs from **conduction** and **convection** in that the transmission of EM waves does not require the presence of matter. (2) Any of the subatomic particles (e.g., **protons, neutrons, alpha particles, electrons**) or **gamma rays** that are emitted by a radioactive **isotope** as a result of the decay of its **nucleus**.

Radioactivity. The emission of **energy** or subatomic particles from an unstable, decaying atomic **nucleus** (the **atom** is called a radioisotope).

> *Also called* radioactive decay
> *See also* **alpha particles, beta particles, gamma rays, half-life**

Raoult's law. A description of the relationship between the **vapor pressure** of a component of a **solution** (P_A) and the **mole fraction** of that component in the solution. The two values are related by the vapor pressure of the pure compound at the same **temperature** as the solution:

$$P_A = P_A^o \cdot X_A^{liq}$$

P_A^o = vapor pressure of the pure component
X_A^{liq} = mole fraction of the component in the solution

Rarefaction. An area where a **longitudinal wave** is "expanded" or where there is a low density of air **molecules**, as occurs with **sound** waves. A rarefaction corresponds to a trough of a **transverse wave**.

Rate-determining step. The **elementary process** in a chemical reaction that has the slowest reaction rate and, hence, the highest **activation energy**.

Rate expression. Relates the rate of change in **concentration** of one reactant (or product) to the concentration of the other reactants in a chemical reaction. Rate expressions, which must be determined by experiment, can be represented by the following formula:

$$Rate = K[A]^m[B]^n$$

K = rate constant
[A] and [B] = the initial concentrations of the reactants
m and n = experimentally-determined exponents (usually small integers)

Real image. An image produced by a mirror or a thin **lens** that has light rays actually passing through it. It is visualized by placing a reflecting surface (e.g., screen, paper) at the point in space where it is formed. By convention, a real image corresponds to a positive image distance (+i).

Compare to **virtual image**

Recessive. Refers to an **allele** whose expression is completely masked by the other allele. **Heterozygotes** often possess one recessive allele; however, they are phenotypically identical to individuals who are **homozygous** dominant (i.e., possess two dominant alleles).

✔ In heterozygotes, the relationship between paired alleles is not always one of **dominance** and recessiveness; **codominance** and **incomplete dominance** are also common types of relationships between paired alleles.

See also **heterozygous, phenotype**
Compare to **dominance**

Recombination. The formation of new **gene** combinations in an organism. The term can be used to more specifically refer to the exchange of genetic sequences between different **chromosomes** or **nucleic acid** strands. In **meiosis**, recombination occurs in several ways, including **crossing-over** and **independent assortment**, both of which result in variations in the genetic composition of the **gametes**. In **bacteria**, recombination can occur by a variety of mechanisms, including **conjugation**, **transduction**, and **transformation**.

Recrystallization. A technique for the purification of **solids**. A concentrated **solution** of an impure substance is prepared at a high **temperature** in a **solvent** that is chosen for its ability to dissolve impurities at low temperatures and dissolve the desired compound only at high temperatures. Upon gradual cooling, the solvent becomes "super-saturated" (i.e., it can no longer retain the same amount of the **solute** that it had previously solubilized at higher temperatures). The solute then recrystallizes, forming a crystal lattice that excludes the impurities because they remain solubilized. The crystals are then filtered from the **solution** and dried.

Redox reaction. A reaction that involves **oxidation** and **reduction** of the reactants.

Reducing agent. A substance that can donate **electrons** to other **atoms** while it undergoes **oxidation**.

Reducing sugar. Any **carbohydrate** that contains a free **hemiacetal** function and can therefore be oxidized by substances such as Benedict's reagent and Tollen's reagent (e.g., **glucose**, maltose). Sucrose is NOT a reducing sugar because the anomeric carbon is part of an **acetal** group.

Reduction. The gain of **electrons** by an **atom** or the gain of hydrogens in biochemical reactions.

Reduction potential ($\mathscr{E}$). A measure, in **volts**, of the **electric potential** of a **half-cell** reaction (i.e., electrode potential) relative to the potential of a standard hydrogen **electrode**, which has $\mathscr{E} = 0$ by definition. Reduction potentials for half-cells at **pressures** of 1 atm and with all **concentrations** at 1 M are presented as standard electrode potentials ($\mathscr{E}°$). By making use of a table of standard electrode potentials, the **cell potential** ($\Delta\mathscr{E}°$) can easily be calculated as:

$$\Delta\mathscr{E}° = \mathscr{E}°(\text{cathode}) - \mathscr{E}°(\text{anode})$$

Reflection. The phenomenon by which light rays strike a surface and bounce back into the medium from which they originated. When light strikes a flat surface, its reflection is governed by the **law of reflection**.

Reflex. An automatic response to external stimuli.

Reflex arc. The simplest functional chain of events in the nervous system that usually only involves one **sensory neuron** and one or more **motor neurons** that **synapse** in the **spinal cord**. The pathway may also involve an **interneuron**.

Refraction. The "bending" of a light ray as it passes from one medium into another. It is caused by the difference in the **speed** that light travels in different media.

    See also **critical angle, index of refraction, lens, Snell's law**

Refractive index. See **index of refraction**

Refractory period. The period of recovery in the region of a **neuron** through which a **nerve impulse** has just passed. The refractory period has two consecutive stages *(Figure 73)*:

1. Absolute refractory period (the Na^+ channels are open; therefore, new **action potentials** cannot be initiated)
2. Relative refractory period [the K^+ channels are open; the **membrane potential** reaches a level below that of the **resting potential** (hyperpolarization); new action potentials can be initiated, but require stronger stimuli than normal in order to cause a **depolarization** that is great enough to overcome the hyperpolarized state of the membrane]

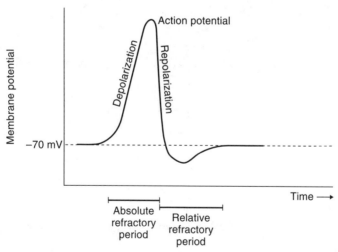

Figure 73. Refractory period

Relative configuration. The **configuration** of a chiral compound relative to another **molecule** for which a standard configuration was arbitrarily determined. In the past, the configuration of (+)-glyceraldehyde was used as the standard; it was assigned an **absolute configuration** of (R) and (−)-glyceraldehyde was correspondingly assigned a configuration of (S).

Currently, however, x-ray crystallography permits the direct determination of a compound's absolute configuration, thus rendering the concept of relative configuration unnecessary. By chance, the absolute configurations assigned to the glyceraldehyde enantiomers turned out to be the correct designations.

Relative specificity. A series of **molecules** are acceptable to a particular **enzyme**, although some are more readily bound than others.

Renin. An **enzyme** produced by specialized **kidney cells**. It initiates a cascade of **blood**-borne factors that leads to the formation of angiotensin II, a potent vasoconstrictor.

Replication. The synthesis of "daughter" **deoxyribonucleic acid (DNA) molecules** using "parent" **nucleic acids** as templates. Each daughter strand is an identical copy of one parent strand (unless DNA **mutations** occur). The replication reaction is catalyzed by **DNA polymerase**, an **enzyme** that adds **nucleotides** to the 3′ end of the **leading strand** and the 3′ ends of the Okazaki fragments that are ligated to form the **lagging strand** *(Figure 74)*. The enzyme complex moves along and between the two strands of the partially-separated DNA double helix; because of its Y-shaped structure, the active site of replication is called the replication fork. The mechanism is referred to as a form of **semiconservative replication**.

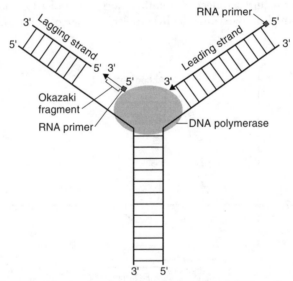

Figure 74. DNA replication. DNA = deoxyribonucleic acid; RNA = ribonucleic acid.

Residual volume (RV). The volume of air that remains in the **lungs** after maximal forced **expiration**; it is normally just over 1 L. It cannot be directly measured, but can be determined by indirect methods.

See also **expiratory reserve volume, functional residual capacity**

Resistance (R). The opposition to a **current** due to the interactions between the flowing **electrons** and the **atoms** of the wire or other devices in the **circuit**. The mathematical definition of resistance is given by **Ohm's law**.

Resistivity (ρ). The inherent property of a material that determines its **resistance**. It is a constant of proportionality in the following formula for the resistance (R) in a wire of length L and cross-sectional area A:

$$R = \rho\left(\frac{L}{A}\right)$$

Resistor. A **conductor** that provides a specific amount of **resistance** in an electrical **circuit**.

Resolution. The separation of a **racemic mixture** into pure **enantiomers**, usually performed using biologic (i.e., enzymatic) techniques.

Resonance. (1) A forced vibration that results in an increase in the **amplitude** of vibration of an object when the **frequency** of **oscillation** of a second vibrating object is near the **natural frequency** of the first object. The frequency at which resonance occurs is called the **resonant frequency**. (2) The delocalization of a compound's **pi bonds** and unpaired **electrons** that is commonly depicted as a combination of different, localized molecular structures. A **molecule** in resonance is a combination, or hybrid, of all possible localized resonance structures that can be drawn. A double-headed arrow ($\leftrightarrow$) is used to relate the different structures that contribute to the actual resonance hybrid; this should not be confused with the equilibrium sign ($\rightleftharpoons$). The compound does not physically "switch" between different forms, but just exists in a form that is not conveniently illustrated.

    Compare to **tautomerism**

Resonant frequency. The **natural frequency** at which an object is forced to vibrate in response to a driving **frequency** that is emitted due to the **oscillation** of another object. Vibrating objects often have more than one resonant frequency.

    ✔ The driving frequency is roughly equal to the resonant frequency.

    See also **resonance, def. (1)**

Respiration. A cellular process by which fuel **molecules** (e.g., **glucose**) undergo **oxidation** to convert their chemical **potential energy** into usable forms of energy, such as **adenosine triphosphate**.

    ✔ Respiration also commonly refers to the physiological process by which oxygen and carbon dioxide are exchanged in the **lungs**. Despite the important relationship between the cellular and **organ**-level processes (i.e., the requirement for oxygen in humans), it is necessary to distinguish between the two to prevent any confusion. We refer to the organ-level process as breathing, gas exchange, or ventilation while reserving the term respiration for the cellular process.

    See also **electron transport chain, fermentation, glycolysis, Krebs cycle, oxidative phosphorylation**

Resting potential. The electric **potential difference** across a **cell membrane** that is created by an unequal **active transport** of ions. An **adenosine triphosphate (ATP)**-utilizing transmembrane pump, called "Na,K-ATPase," maintains a relative excess of positive charge on the outer side of the membrane and a corresponding excess of negative charge on the inside. At rest (i.e., not depolarized, not transmitting an **action potential**), the membrane transports 3 Na^+ out of the **cell** for every 2 K^+ that it brings in. Moreover, the membrane is only passively permeable to K^+, which is free to diffuse back out of the cell; Na^+ remains trapped on the outside and all negative **anions** (e.g., Cl^-) are trapped on the inside. Because K^+ is the only ion allowed to attain a steady-state equilibrium (i.e., no net **diffusion** in any direction), the **membrane potential** at rest is close to that which would exist if K^+ was the only ion involved (approximately -70 mV). A cell at its resting potential is "polarized;" alternatively, it is "repolarized" if the membrane has just recovered from a **depolarization.**

Retina. The innermost layer of the eyeball that receives the image formed by the **lens** and transmits it to the **brain.** The retina interprets the light with the numerous **photoreceptors** on its surface.

See also **fovea**

Reynolds' number (R_e). A measure of whether the flow of a **fluid** is streamlined or turbulent, as calculated using the following equation:

$$R_e = 2vr\rho/\eta$$

v = average **speed** of the fluid
r = radius of the tube in which the fluid is flowing
ρ = **density** of the fluid
η = **viscosity** of the fluid

Experiments have shown that if $R_e < 2000$, the flow is streamlined; if $R_e > 2000$, the flow is turbulent.

See also **streamline flow, turbulent flow**

Rhizoid. A root-like structure in some **fungi.**

Rhodopsin. The **pigment** in **rods.**

Rib cage. A cone-shaped, flexible assembly of **bones** that encloses and protects the abdominal and thoracic **organs** and supports the upper extremities. It also plays a major role in the mechanics of **inspiration.**

Ribonucleic acid (RNA). A **nucleic acid** composed of a linear sequence of ribonucleotides (i.e., **nucleotides** in which the 5-carbon sugar is ribose). RNA differs from DNA in that it is normally single-stranded and contains the **nitrogenous base** uracil in place of thymine. In eukaryotes and prokaryotes, a given strand of RNA is complementary to the unique sequence of **deoxyribonucleic acid (DNA)** from which it was transcribed. Although every RNA **molecule** found in the **cell** is of similar general structure, the term used to describe a particular strand (e.g., **messenger RNA, ribosomal RNA,** or **transfer RNA**) depends on the function that it serves. RNA also constitutes the **genomes** of many types of **viruses.**

See also **transcription, translation**

Ribonucleic acid (RNA) polymerase. The **enzyme** that catalyzes **transcription.** It elongates RNA chains by adding **nucleotides** to 3'-hydroxy termini.

Ribonucleic acid (RNA) primers. Short sequences of RNA upon whose 3'-OH ends the synthesis of the **leading strand** and all Okazaki fragments is initiated during **replication** of **deoxyribonucleic acid (DNA)** *[Figure 75]*. On the **lagging strand**, these primers are replaced by the DNA of the subsequent Okazaki fragment. However, on both daughter strands, the initial RNA primer must be dealt with by alternative means (i.e., **telomeres**) because there is no preceding DNA that can be extended in a 5' to 3' direction to replace the RNA.

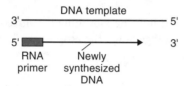

Figure 75. Ribonucleic acid primer. DNA = deoxyribonucleic acid; RNA = ribonucleic acid.

Ribosomal ribonucleic acid (rRNA). The **nucleic acids** that are components of **ribosomes**. They are transcribed from **deoxyribonucleic acid** in the **nucleolus**.

Ribosome. The cellular structure, composed of several **proteins** and **nucleic acids** (e.g., **ribosomal ribonucleic acid**), that carries out the **translation** of **polypeptide** chains using **messenger ribonucleic acid** transcripts. Ribosomes can be free in the **cytoplasm**; however, in eukaryotic **cells**, they are often bound to the surface of the rough **endoplasmic reticulum**.

RNA. See **ribonucleic acid**

Rod. A type of retinal **photoreceptor** that is extremely sensitive to dim light and thus facilitates black-and-white and peripheral vision. It contains **rhodopsin**, a **pigment** that causes the transmission of a **nerve impulse** upon receiving a single **photon** of light.

Compare to **cone**

Rotational motion. The movement of an object about an axis caused by a **force** applied at a **distance** from the axis (called a **torque**). The torque is not directed along the axis, but is perpendicular to it.

Round window. The membrane-covered opening of the **cochlea** that is at the end of the tube opposite to the **oval window**. The round window relieves the **pressure** that **sound** waves exert as they pass through the **inner ear**.

rRNA. See **ribosomal ribonucleic acid**

S

Sacculus. See **utricle**

Saliva. A mucous **solution** secreted into the mouth by the three salivary **glands**. It moistens and lubricates food to ease its passage down the **esophagus**. It also contains **amylase** and certain antimicrobial compounds.

Salt. Any **electrolyte** that does not contain H^+ or OH^-. A salt is the product of a reaction between an **acid** and a **base**.

Saltatory conduction. The rapid transmission of a **nerve impulse** in myelinated portions of an **axon**. The conduction of the **action potential** is quickened because there is not a wave of **depolarization**, but rather a "skipping" of an electrical **current** from one **node of Ranvier** to the next, bypassing the regions covered by the insulating **myelin sheath** *(Figure 76)*.

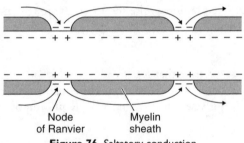

Node   Myelin
of Ranvier   sheath

Figure 76. Saltatory conduction

Saponification. The alkaline **hydrolysis** of an **ester** (usually a **fat molecule**) that yields the **salt** of a **fatty acid** and an **alcohol** (e.g., **glycerol**).

✔ Alkaline hydrolysis takes place in the presence of a **base**.

Sarcolemma. The **plasma membrane** of a **skeletal muscle cell**.

Sarcomere. A contractile assembly of **actin** and **myosin** filaments bounded on either side by "Z lines" *(Figure 77)*. **Myofibrils** are composed of series of repeating sarcomeres that contract in synchronization and act as the functional units of **skeletal muscle**.

Sarcoplasmic reticulum. The term that refers specifically to the smooth **endoplasmic reticulum** within **muscle cells**. It regulates the release of calcium **ions** that are necessary for transmission of the **action potential** that leads to **muscle contraction**.

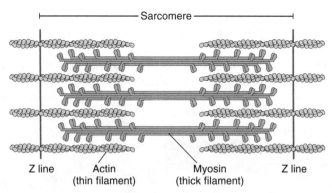

Figure 77. Sarcomere

Saturated solution. A **solution** that contains the maximum amount of **solute** at a given **temperature**. Any solute added to a saturated solution remains as excess, undissolved **solid** called precipitate.

See also **precipitation**

Scalar. A quantity or value that only has magnitude, not direction.

Compare to **vector**

Schwann cells. **Glial cells** that surround the neuronal **axon** and form the **myelin sheath**. The cells concentrate themselves at regular intervals along the axon to act as electrical insulation that allows **saltatory conduction** to occur.

Sclera. A dense, opaque **connective tissue** that is continuous with the **cornea** and makes up most of the protective outer layer of the eyeball. It is commonly known as "the white" of the eye.

Scrotum. The sack that contains the **testes** and maintains them at a **temperature** approximately 3°C lower than the rest of the body, a condition necessary for proper **sperm** development.

Second law of thermodynamics. The total **entropy** of a system and its surroundings increases as a result of any natural, spontaneous process. All systems tend toward molecular disorder (i.e., higher entropy).

Secretin. A **hormone** secreted by special **cells** of the **duodenum** when there is a low **pH** in the **small intestine**. It stimulates the **pancreas** to secrete bicarbonate, a **base** that neutralizes the hydrochloric acid [$HCl_{(aq)}$] that flowed into the duodenum from the **stomach**.

Segregation of alleles (Mendel's first law). Because the **chromosomes** in each **homologous pair** segregate during **meiosis** I, the **alleles** of a pair are randomly separated from one another. Each **gamete** has an equal probability of possessing either member of an **allelic pair**.

✔ Only one allele for a given **gene** exists in each gamete.

See also **law of independent assortment**

Semen. A semiliquid mixture of **sperm** and seminal **fluid** that is ejected from the **penis** during male orgasm. It contains **spermatozoa** and nutrients (e.g., fructose).

Semicircular ducts. Three **fluid**-filled canals in the **vestibular system** of the **inner ear**, each of which is oriented in a plane that is perpendicular to the other two (see Appendix A, Figure 12). The canals permit the detection of changes in angular **acceleration** of the head via a mechanism by which a rotation of the head causes the fluid in a particular duct (which of the three ducts depends on the direction and angle of rotation) to pool in its **ampulla**, resulting in the stimulation of appropriate **sensory neurons**.

> *See also* **sacculus, utricle**

Semiconservative replication. Each strand of the **deoxyribonucleic acid (DNA)** double helix serves as a template upon which a new, complementary strand is made. The term "semiconservative" derives from the fact that one complete parental DNA strand is conserved as one of the strands in each of the two new daughter helices.

> *See also* **replication**

Seminal vesicle. The **gland** that contributes the seminal fluid to the male ejaculate.

Seminiferous tubules. Tightly-coiled tubes in the **testes** that are the site of **spermatogenesis**.

Sensory neuron. An **afferent neuron** that conducts **nerve impulses** from a sensory **organ** (e.g., **photoreceptor**, taste bud) to the **central nervous system**.

> *Compare to* **motor neuron**

Series circuit. A connection of electrical **circuit** elements that have only one point in common (i.e., the **current** passes through only one **element** at a time). The current is the same in each device; however, the total voltage is equal to the sum of the voltage drops in each element. For a circuit with *n* **resistors**, the net **resistance** (R) is also the algebraic sum of the resistance in each circuit element, as derived from **Ohm's law** *(Figure 78)*:

$$R = R_1 + R_2 + R_3 + \ldots + R_n$$

> ✔ A circuit element is either a **capacitor**, a resistor, or an inductor.

> *Compare to* **parallel circuit**

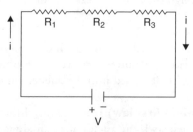

Figure 78. Series circuit. i = current; R = net resistance; V = voltage.

Sertoli cells. Support **cells** located in the **testes** that aid in the development of **spermatogonia** into **spermatozoa**.

Serum. The contents of **blood plasma** after the clotting factors (e.g., fibrinogen) and **blood** cells have been removed.

Sex chromosome. An X or Y **chromosome** that is involved in determining the sex of an individual. It is the sex chromosome carried by the **spermatozoon** that determines the sex of the **embryo** because all **gametes** produced by the female contain an X chromosome.

See also **sex-linked trait**

Compare to **autosomes**

Sex-linked trait. A genetic trait for which the **gene** is located on the X **chromosome** (but not on the Y chromosome). Because males and females have a different number of X chromosomes, the **phenotype** for a sex-linked trait is related to the sex of the individual. The common pattern, as seen in some forms of hemophilia and color blindness, is that males who inherit the trait are afflicted while females are "carriers" (i.e., one X chromosome has the **mutation** while the other is wild type); therefore, it is rare for a female to suffer from a disease associated with a sex-linked mutation.

✔ Wild type refers to the most common or nonmutant **allele** that exists in the **population**.

Also called X-linked trait

Shared pair. Two **electrons** that constitute a **covalent bond** between two **atoms**. They are found in the intramolecular space between the two **nuclei**.

Compare to **lone pair**

Shear modulus (G). A constant of proportionality that relates the **shear stress** $\left(\dfrac{F}{A}\right)$ exerted on an object to the shear **strain** $\left(\dfrac{\Delta L}{L_o}\right)$, as illustrated in *Figure 79* and shown in the following equation:

$$\frac{F}{A} = G \cdot \left(\frac{\Delta L}{L_o}\right)$$

F = force
A = area
ΔL = change in length
L_o = height of object

✔ The shear modulus can be considered as a measure of the **solid**'s rigidity.

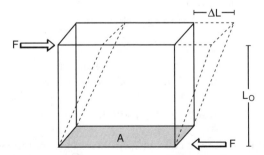

Figure 79. Shear modulus. A = area; F = force; ΔL = change in length; L_o = height of the object.

Shear stress. Parallel **forces** applied in opposite directions to the opposite surfaces of a **solid** (see Figure 79).

Compare to **compression, tension**

Shell. A grouping of **atomic orbitals** based on their **energy** level, as indicated by the **principal quantum number (n)**. For example, all orbitals with n = 1 are in the K shell, all orbitals with n = 2 are in the L shell, and so forth.

Sigma (σ) bond. An intramolecular chemical linkage formed by the direct overlap of **atomic orbitals** of two different **atoms** in which the **electron density** lies between the **nuclei** of the two atoms and is symmetrical about the axis of the bond. Carbon-carbon single bonds are sigma bonds in which two sp^3 orbitals, one from each carbon atom, are overlapping.

Compare to **pi bond**

Simple harmonic motion (SHM). The periodic motion of an object that is a sinusoidal function of time. The restoring **force** responsible for the **oscillations** is described by **Hooke's law**.

Sinoatrial node. An excitable patch of **tissue** that is often referred to as the "pacemaker" of the **heart**. It originates the heartbeat and initiates the contraction of the **atria**.

Skeletal muscle. A group of **muscle fibers** whose contractions are voluntarily controlled via **motor neurons** of the **somatic nervous system**. Skeletal muscle is composed of muscle fibers made up of **myofibrils**, which are composed of repeating **sarcomeres**. This structure results in the characteristic striations that are clearly visible under low microscopic power *(Figure 80)*. The striations represent regions where the actin and myosin filaments overlap (also referred to as the "A band"). Skeletal muscle contracts rapidly but tires easily.

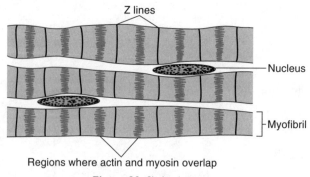

Figure 80. Skeletal muscle

Small intestine. The longest section of the gastrointestinal tract that leads from the **stomach** to the **colon**. It is the **organ** in which most food is broken down and where almost all absorption of food **molecules** occurs. The small intestine is structurally and functionally divided into three portions: the **duodenum, jejunum,** and **ileum**.

Smooth muscle. A group of **muscle cells** whose contractions are primarily involuntary due to almost exclusive innervation by the **autonomic nervous system**. Smooth muscle is composed of distinct spindle-shaped, uninucleated **cells** that can be visibly distinguished from **skeletal muscle** due to the lack of striations *(Figure 81)*. The cells contain thin and thick filaments, but their arrangement is not in the orderly pattern seen in **striated muscle** types. Smooth muscle contracts slowly but can maintain contractions for extended periods of time.

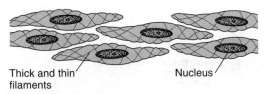

Thick and thin
filaments   Nucleus

Figure 81. Smooth muscle

Snell's law. An equation that describes the relationship between the angle of incidence (Θ_1) and the angle of **refraction** (Θ_2) of a light ray as it crosses the barrier between two media. The angles can be related in terms of the indices of refraction (n), the **speed** of light in each of the two media (v), or the **wavelength** in each of the two media (λ) *[Figure 82]*.

See also **index of refraction**

$$\frac{\sin \Theta_1}{\sin \Theta_2} = \frac{v_1}{v_2} = \frac{\lambda_1}{\lambda_2} = \frac{n_2}{n_1}$$

Figure 82. Snell's law. n = indices of refraction; v = speed of light in the media; Θ_1 = angle of incidence; Θ_2 = angle of refraction; λ = wavelength in the media.

Sodium-potassium pump. A transmembrane **protein** channel that uses **adenosine triphosphate** to actively pump Na^+ out of the **cell** while pumping K^+ into the cell. This mechanism is responsible for establishing the **resting potential** of electrically-excitable membranes (e.g., membranes of **neurons**).

Also called Na-K-ATPase

Solid. A material that possesses both definite volume and shape and consists of ordered **molecules** that have small **distances** between them relative to **gas** or **liquid** molecules. Solids are usually of higher **densities** than liquids or gases and are relatively incompressible.

Solubility product (K_{sp}). The **equilibrium constant** for the dissolution of an insoluble (i.e., very slightly soluble) **electrolyte**. It represents the equilibrium between the **precipitation** of the **solid** out of a **saturated solution** and the dissolution of **solute** into **solution**. The smaller the product, the less soluble the solute.

Solute. A substance dissolved in a **solvent** to make a **solution**. It can be a **solid**, **liquid**, or **gas**.

Solution. A homogeneous mixture of two or more substances (e.g., **gases**, **liquids**, or **solids**). The homogeneity of the mixture is evidenced by the fact that the different compounds in the solution cannot be individually distinguished from one another. The classic example is table salt dissolved in water (homogeneous mixture) compared to a typical oil and vinegar salad dressing (heterogeneous mixture).

Solvent. The component of a **solution** in which one or more solutes are dissolved. It is usually a **liquid**.

Somatic cells. All of an individual's **cells**, except those that give rise to the **gametes**.

Somatic nervous system. The network of all peripheral **motor neurons** (**efferent** pathways) that stimulate voluntary **skeletal muscle** contraction.

> *Compare to* **autonomic nervous system**

Somatotropin. A **hormone** that stimulates **muscle** and **bone** growth. It is secreted by the **anterior pituitary gland**.

> *Also called* growth hormone

Sound. Longitudinal waves produced by vibrating matter (i.e., the source) and detected by a detector (e.g., the ear). The **waves** must travel through an elastic medium (e.g., air, water, wood). In air, at 0°C and 1 atm, sound travels at 331 m/s.

> *See also* **intensity, pitch**

Specific gravity. The ratio of the **density** of a substance to the density of water at 4.0°C or another specified temperature.

Specific heat (C). A measure of the amount of **heat** (Q) a body or object can gain or lose per unit change in **temperature** (Δt) and unit mass (m) of the substance of which the object is composed:

$$C = \frac{Q}{(m \cdot \Delta t)}$$

> ✔ The specific heat of water is 1 cal/g°C.

Specific immune response. An **immune response** involving **lymphocytes** that are directed against a particular **antigen**. After an initial encounter with a foreign antigen, the specific immune system establishes immunologic memory, which permits the body to mount an increasingly effective defense upon subsequent encounters with the antigen. The specific immune response also amplifies and focuses the body's natural, or nonspecific, immune mechanisms (i.e., those that are present prior to exposure to infectious agents, are not enhanced by such exposures, and do not discriminate among different foreign substances).

> ✔ A specific immune response is more accurately called an adaptive immune response.

Speed. The rate at which an object is moving. It is equal to the **distance** travelled as a function of time (a **scalar**). Speed is the magnitude of **velocity**.

Speed of light (c). The **speed** at which all **electromagnetic radiation** travels through a vacuum. It is equal to approximately 3.00×10^8 m/s.

Sperm. The mature and motile male **gamete**.

> *Also called* **spermatozoon**

Spermatid. One of the four **haploid cells** that results from the meiotic division of a single **spermatocyte**. Each spermatid develops into a mature **spermatozoon**.

Spermatocyte. A **diploid cell** that gives rise to **spermatids** via **meiosis**. A primary spermatocyte, which is formed directly from the mitotic division of **spermatogonia** within the **seminiferous tubules**, undergoes meiosis I, which leads to the formation of two secondary spermatocytes. The secondary spermatocytes enter into meiosis II and give rise to four spermatids.

Spermatogenesis. The development of mature **sperm cells** from **spermatogonia** within the **seminiferous tubules** in the **testes** (see Appendix A, Figure 5B). The entire process takes approximately 64 days.

Spermatogonium. An undifferentiated **diploid** germ **cell** that differentiates, via **mitosis**, to produce primary **spermatocytes** in the male.

Spermatozoon. A mature **haploid sperm** cell that is characterized by its compact **nucleus**, numerous **mitochondria**, **acrosome**, and single **flagellum**.

Spinal cord. The structure in the **central nervous system** that serves as a link between the **brain** and the **peripheral nervous system**. It is characterized by:
- an interior composed of **gray matter** (i.e., **nerve cell** bodies)
- an exterior composed of **white matter** (i.e., myelinated **axons**)
- dorsal, **afferent sensory neurons**
- ventral, **efferent motor neurons**

> ✔ To remember the types of sensory and motor neurons, use the following acronyms: DAVE (dorsal afferent, ventral efferent) and SAME (sensory afferent, motor efferent).

Spinal nerves. The 31 peripheral **nerves** that connect to the **central nervous system** through the **spinal cord**.

Spindle apparatus. A web of **microtubules** that assembles at the equator of a dividing **cell** during **prophase** of **meiosis** or **mitosis**. The apparatus directs the migration of **chromosomes** to opposite poles of the cell.

> *See also* **centromere, kinetochore, metaphase**

Spindle fibers. The **microtubules** of which the **spindle apparatus** is composed.

Spin quantum number (m_s). The component of the **electron configuration** that describes the spin orientation of the **atomic orbital**. This value, which can only be either $+\frac{1}{2}$ or $-\frac{1}{2}$, refers to a specific **electron**.

Spirillum. A helical, coil-shaped **bacterium**.

Spirometer. A device for directly measuring **lung** volume and flow rates.

> ✔ The **residual volume** cannot be measured using a spirometer.

Spleen. A major **blood**-filtering **organ** that has both immunologic and circulatory functions. It contains lymphoid **tissue**; thus, it is a component of the **lymphatic vessel system** and is similar to other **lymph nodes**. It also serves as a reservoir of **platelets**, **erythrocytes**, and **neutrophils** and is the site where old platelets and erythrocytes are destroyed.

Spongy bone. A porous lattice of **bone tissue** of which **flat bones** are composed. It is also found in **long bones** at the ends and in the interiors, where it is surrounded by denser **compact bone**. Red **bone marrow** exists in the spongy bone lattice.

Standard enthalpy of formation (ΔH_f°). The **enthalpy change** that occurs when one **mole** of a compound is formed from its **elements** at 298 K and 1 atm.

Standard state. (1) At a temperature of 298 K, the most stable form of an **element** at a pressure of 1 atm. (2) A **gas** at a **partial pressure** of 1 atm. (3) A dissolved **ion** at a **concentration** of 1.00 M.

Standard temperature and pressure (STP). A **temperature** of 0°C (approximately 298 K) and a **pressure** of 1 atm.

Standing wave. A **wave** that occurs when a rope that is fixed at one end is made to vibrate at its **natural frequency**. The standing wave results from the **interference** that occurs when waves travelling along the rope are reflected at the stationary end and sent back into oncoming waves. The reason the wave appears to be "standing" is because the **nodes** and **antinodes** remain in fixed positions *(Figure 83)*. Although the standing wave can be explained in terms of interference, the rope also serves as an example of a vibrating object in **resonance** because the standing wave only occurs when the rope is forced to vibrate at one of its **resonant frequencies**. Standing waves are not just produced in fixed ropes or strings; in fact, standing waves are set up that correspond to the natural frequency of any object that is set into vibration. This principle is the basis for all musical **sounds**, whether produced by vibrating strings, air (wind instruments), or **solid** material (percussion instruments).

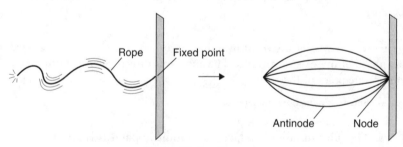

Figure 83. Standing wave

Starch. A branched **polymer** of **glucose** that serves as the primary form of fuel storage in plants.

    Compare to **glycogen**

State function. A property of a thermodynamic system that has a value that is absolute for a given state of the system (e.g., **enthalpy**). It only depends on the initial and final states and not on the path taken to arrive at the final state.

Stem cells. Highly undifferentiated, multipotential **cells** with a high rate of cell division that can give rise to numerous types of differentiated cells. For example, **bone marrow** stem cells give rise to a diverse array of **blood** cells.

> *See also* **differentiation**

Stereoisomers. A general category of isomeric chemical compounds (**isomers**) that have the same sequence of covalently-bonded **atoms** (thus, they are not structural isomers), but different arrangements of their atoms in 3-dimensional space. Stereoisomers can differ in either **conformation** (e.g., eclipsed, staggered conformers) or **configuration** (e.g., **geometric isomers, enantiomers**).

> *Compare to* **constitutional isomers**

Steric strain. Repulsion between chemical groups in a compound due to their spatial proximity (e.g., **methyl groups** in gauche and eclipsed **conformations**).

Steroids. A class of **lipids** that are complex, tetracyclic **molecules** (i.e., four fused carbon rings) of substantial physiologic importance (e.g., cholesterol, cortisone, **testosterone**).

Stoichiometry. Use of the atomic theory to make quantitative assessments related to **atoms**, compounds, and chemical reactions.

Stomach. A sac-like portion of the gastrointestinal tract where the digestive process is initiated.

> *See also* **chief cells, parietal cells**

Strain. A deformation that results from a **stress** applied to a **solid**. It is measured as the ratio of the change in length to the original length of the object. Depending on the type of stress applied, the strain can be mathematically related to the magnitude of stress using constants of proportionality called **Young's modulus, bulk modulus,** or **shear modulus**.

Streamline flow. A flow of **fluid** that is smooth (i.e., the side-by-side layers of fluid slide by each other without any noticeable disturbances).

> *Also called* laminar flow
> *Compare to* **turbulent flow**

Stress. A deforming **force** (F), per unit area (A), that is applied to a **solid**:

$$\text{stress} = \frac{F}{A}$$

Striated muscle. See **cardiac muscle, skeletal muscle**

Strong acid. An **acid** that undergoes virtually complete dissociation into its **ions** when diluted in aqueous **solution**. Some examples include HCl and H_3PO_4.

> *Compare to* **weak acid**

Strong base. A **base** that undergoes virtually complete dissociation into its **ions** when diluted in aqueous **solution**. Some examples include NaOH and KOH.

> *Compare to* **weak base**

Subcutaneous tissue. The innermost layer of skin that primarily contains adipose **tissue** (i.e., fat **cells**). Its main function is the thermal insulation of the body.

Submucosa. A layer of **connective tissue** that underlies and supports the **mucosa** of the gastrointestinal and respiratory tracts.

Substitution reaction. A chemical reaction in which one **atom**, **ion**, or functional group is substituted for another.

> *See also* **electrophilic aromatic substitution, nucleophilic substitution**

Substrate. A biological reactant or product. The interconversion between different substrates is often catalyzed by **enzymes**.

Superposition principle. States that the effects of two or more **waves** on the **displacement** of a single particle are independent of one another. As such, waves that encounter one another are "summed" and result in **constructive interference** or **destructive interference**.

Suppressor T cells. A subtype of **T lymphocytes** that dampen the activity of T and B **cells** after the cause of the **immune response** has been eliminated.

Surface tension. The **tension** that arises from the attractive **forces** of **cohesion** between **molecules**. It acts parallel to the surface of a **fluid**.

> ✔ Water has such a high surface tension that some insects can walk on the surface of a pool of water.

Suspension. A heterogeneous mixture of an insoluble **solid** in a **liquid** (e.g., starch in water). The suspended solid settles at the bottom of the container as a result of **gravity** at a rate that is dependent on particle size and density.

Swallowing center. The part of the **medulla oblongata** that stimulates **peristalsis** in the **esophagus** via specific **cranial nerves**.

Sympathetic nervous system. The branch of the **autonomic nervous system** in which **efferent nerve** pathways serve to remove the body from its normal resting state. The effects on the body, such as an increase in the **heart** rate and dilation of the **pupils**, are widespread and constitute the "flight-or-fight" response. Many of the effects are antagonistic to parasympathetic effects. **Acetylcholine** acts as the **neurotransmitter** at the **ganglia**; however, **noradrenaline** is the most common neurotransmitter at the terminal **synapses** that exist in the target **organs**.

> ✔ Sympathetic ganglionic synapses are closer to the **spinal cord** than to the target organs.

> *Compare to* **parasympathetic nervous system**

Synapse. The junction between the **axon** tip of a **neuron** and the membrane of another **cell**, which could be a neuron, a **gland** cell, a **muscle cell**, and so forth. **Nerve impulses** are conducted across synapses by chemical mediators called **neurotransmitters**. Synapses can be excitatory, meaning that the **membrane potential** of the receiving neuron is driven toward **depolarization**, or inhibitory, in which case the receiving neuron is inhibited from firing an **action potential**.

Synapsis. The exact pairing of **homologous pairs** of **chromosomes** that occurs during **prophase** I of **meiosis**. It is during synapsis that **crossing-over** takes place.

Syncytium. An interconnected network of **cardiac muscle** cells that facilitates the rapid transmission of **action potentials** from one **cell** to the next.

Systemic circulation. The network of **blood vessels** that supplies **blood** to the head, extremities, and trunk. The major vessels involved are the **aorta** and **vena cava**.

> *Compare to* **pulmonary circulation**

Systole. The period of the cardiac contraction cycle when the **ventricles** are contracting. During this time, the **atria** are relaxed and the **pressure** in the **aorta** is increasing as **blood** is forced out of the ventricles and into the **systemic circulation**.

Tautomerism, keto-enol. An interconversion of the chemical structure of a carbonyl compound in which the acidic α-hydrogen of a **ketone** or **aldehyde** is transferred to the oxygen **atom** while a double bond forms between the carbonyl carbon and the α-carbon (the carbon covalently bonded to the carbonyl carbon). The keto tautomer has the normal carbonyl structure; the enol tautomer has the **hydroxyl group** and double-bond formation *(Figure 84)*. Most reaction equilibria favor the keto form.

✔ The keto and enol tautomers are not **resonance** structures because there are actually two different structures in equilibrium, as opposed to a hybrid resonance structure.

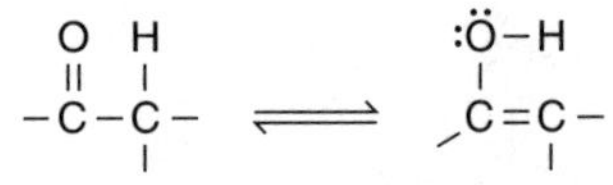

Keto form   Enol form
Figure 84. Tautomerism

Telomere. A simple repeating sequence of **deoxyribonucleic acid (DNA)** at each end of a eukaryotic **chromosome** that serves as the template for the terminal **ribonucleic acid (RNA) primers** synthesized during DNA **replication**. The telomere provides a solution to a fundamental problem of chromosomal replication—how to prevent the loss of the RNA primers' template sequences at the 5′-ends of both "daughter" DNA strands. The problem exists because **DNA polymerase** is unable to initiate synthesis *de novo* (i.e., without a primer) and is only able to add **nucleotides** at the 3′-OH termini of **nucleic acids**. It is thus unable to work "backward," a feature it would need to be capable of replacing the terminal RNA primers with DNA. The telomere, however, can be periodically extended due to its repeating structure; thus, it replaces those nucleotides that are lost during each replication cycle. Bacteria have an alternative solution to the same problem—circular **genomes**.

Telophase. The last stage of **mitosis** in which the **chromosomes** uncoil and prepare themselves for **gene** expression. A **nuclear membrane** re-forms around each of the two **diploid** sets of chromosomes and the **spindle apparatus** is dismantled. This stage leads to **cytokinesis**. In **meiosis**, there are two stages of telophase.

- Telophase I is characterized by the clustering of the two sets of chromosomes at their respective poles. The **deoxyribonucleic acid (DNA)** in these chromosomes was replicated before meiosis began and, therefore, each chromosome consists of a pair of sister **chromatids** attached at a **centromere**. However, the chromatids are not identical due to the **crossing-over** that occurred in **prophase** I.
- Telophase II is similar to the mitotic telophase, except that the **nuclei** formed at the end of meiosis are **haploid**.

See also **anaphase, interphase, metaphase, prophase**

Temperature. An **intensive property** of the state of a thermodynamic system that provides a measure of the average **kinetic energy** of the **molecules** in the system. Temperature is measured in degrees Fahrenheit (°F), degrees centigrade or Celsius (°C), or degrees Kelvin (K). The divisions in both of the latter two scales, which are commonly used in scientific contexts, have the same magnitude. However, the Celsius scale is based on the melting point of water at 0°C and the **boiling point** of water at 100°C (at 1 atm) while the Kelvin scale is an absolute temperature scale based on a zero point (0 K), which is the lowest possible theoretical temperature. The Celsius and Kelvin scales are related by the following equation:

$$°C = K - 273.15$$

The Fahrenheit degree is smaller than the Celsius degree. These two scales are related by the following equation:

$$°F = \left(\frac{9}{5}\right)°C + 32$$

✔ Although there is a difference between the definitions for centigrade and Celsius, in practice they are identical.

Temporal lobe. The component of the **cerebrum** that contains the auditory cortex.

Tendon. A type of **connective tissue** that links **muscles** and **bones**.

Tension. A type of **stress** that consists of equal **forces** acting in opposite directions on the same **solid**. When tension is applied to a solid, that solid is said to be stretched or strained.

Also called tensile stress

See also **Young's modulus**

Compare to **compression, shear stress**

Testes. A pair of male **sperm**-producing **organs** enclosed within the **scrotum**. They are also **glands** that secrete **testosterone**.

Testosterone. The primary male sex **hormone** that stimulates both **spermatogenesis** and the development and maintenance of secondary male sexual characteristics. It is produced by the **interstitial cells** of the **testes**. Testosterone is a **steroid**.

Tetanus. A state in which a series of **muscle contractions** occur in a single **muscle fiber** in close enough succession that they cause a single, smooth, sustained development of **force**.

Thalamus. A component of the **forebrain** that is the primary site of integration of sensory input into the **brain**.

Thermal energy. The sum of the **potential energy** and **kinetic energy** associated with a single body, object, or system.

Also called internal energy

Thermal equilibrium. The situation in which the **heat flow** between two bodies is zero. At this point, the **temperatures** of the two bodies are equal.

Thermoregulation. The regulation of a person's core body **temperature**, which is controlled by the **hypothalamus**.

Threshold value. The minimum stimulus required to cause an **action potential** in a **neuron**. The common analogy compares neurons to guns and the stimulus to the pulling of the trigger; no matter how hard you pull the trigger, as long as you pull it past a certain point (i.e., past the threshold), the bullet will be fired at the same **velocity**.

Thymosin. A **hormone** secreted by the **thymus** that promotes the production of **leukocytes**.

Thymus. A small lymphoid **organ** that plays a critical role in the development of mature **T lymphocytes**, especially in early life.

> ✔ The term lymphoid implies that this organ contains **lymphocytes** and is part of the **lymphatic vessel system**.

Thyroid gland. An **endocrine** organ that produces **thyroxine** and **calcitonin**.

Thyroid-stimulating hormone (TSH). A **hormone** produced by the **anterior pituitary gland** that stimulates the **thyroid gland** to produce **thyroxine**. It is considered a trophic hormone because it stimulates the growth of the thyroid gland.

Thyroxine. A **hormone** produced by the **thyroid gland** that stimulates **cell metabolism**. It is essential for normal growth and development.

Tidal volume. The volume of air inhaled during each normal **inspiration** (approximately 0.5 L).

Tight junction. A region where the **plasma membranes** of two adjacent **cells** are fused together to create a barrier against the leakage of **fluid** through a **tissue**.

Tissue. A set of **cells** that are structurally similar and act together to carry out a specific function.

Titration, acid-base. A **neutralization** reaction in which the **concentration** of an **acid** (or **base**) is determined by gradually adding a base (or acid) of known concentration until the **equivalence point** is reached.

T lymphocytes. A class of **lymphocytes** that play a major role in **cell-mediated immune responses**. They are produced in the **bone marrow**, but mature in the **thymus**. Unlike **B lymphocytes**, T lymphocytes recognize and respond to **antigens** that are associated with the cell surface but are not soluble. Antigen-stimulated T lymphocytes are important sources of the **cytokines** that regulate the proliferation and **differentiation** of T lymphocytes and other cells, including B lymphocytes and **macrophages**.

> *Also called* T cells
> *See also* **cytotoxic T cells, helper T cells**

Tonicity. The relative **concentrations** of a **solute** in two separate **solutions**.

Torque (τ). The effective **force** that causes a rotation about an axis, as given by the following equation:

$$\tau = F \cdot r$$

F = the applied force

r = the moment arm (the perpendicular **distance** from the axis to the line of the applied force)

Torque can also be defined in terms of the angular **acceleration** *(Figure 85):*

$$\tau = mr^2\alpha$$

m = mass

r = the moment arm

α = angular acceleration

✔ Torque is a **vector** with the units of Newton-meter (N·m).

Figure 85. Torque. F = applied force; m = mass; r = the moment arm.

Torsional strain. **Electron** pair repulsions between bonds on adjacent **atoms** that result in restricted rotation about that bond. The maximum torsional strain occurs in eclipsed **conformations** of organic compounds.

See also **steric strain**

Total internal reflection. At the barrier between two media, a light ray that originates in the denser of the two media is reflected back into the denser medium if its angle of incidence is greater than the **critical angle**.

✔ This can be illustrated using **Snell's law**.

See also **index of refraction**

Trace minerals. Naturally-occurring metals that are required in minute amounts for proper human nutrition.

Trachea. The tubular component of the respiratory system that connects the **bronchi** to the mouth. It is commonly referred to as the "windpipe."

Tract (in the nervous system). A bundle of **neurons** in the **central nervous system**. It is analogous to a **nerve** in the **peripheral nervous system**.

Transcription. The biochemical process by which a strand of **ribonucleic acid (RNA)** is synthesized using a **deoxyribonucleic acid (DNA)** template. The reaction is catalyzed by **RNA polymerase**, an **enzyme** that adds **nucleotides** to the 3'-OH end of the growing RNA **molecule** as it travels along the DNA strand in the 3' to 5' direction. In eukaryotic **cells**, this process occurs in the **nucleus** and is followed by the migration of the RNA through **nuclear pores** into the **cytoplasm**, where **translation** takes place. In prokaryotic cells, transcription takes place in the cytoplasm and is often coupled with translation.

✔ The RNA polymerase moves along the DNA in a 3' to 5' direction as it synthesizes RNA in the antiparallel 5' to 3' direction.

Transduction. The transfer of whole or parts of **deoxyribonucleic acid molecules** between **bacteria**, resulting in an organism with a changed genetic constitution. It is facilitated by a phage vector.

> ✔ Phage is short for **bacteriophage** and a vector is, in this context, a mobile carrier of genetic material.

Compare to **conjugation, transformation**

Transfer ribonucleic acid (tRNA). A class of small **ribonucleic acid (RNA) molecules** that transport the appropriate **amino acids** to the growing **polypeptide** chain in the **ribosomes** during the **translation** of a **messenger ribonucleic acid** strand.

Transformation. (1) The incorporation of free **deoxyribonucleic acid** into a **bacterium** from the surrounding medium. (2) Conversion of a normal cultured eukaryotic cell to a cancer-like state of uncontrolled proliferation.

Compare to **conjugation, transduction**

Transition state. See **activated state**

Translation. The biochemical process by which a **polypeptide** chain is assembled according to the specific **messenger ribonucleic acid** sequence of **codons** "translated" by **ribosomes**. This process occurs in the **cytoplasm** in both **prokaryotes** and **eukaryotes**.

Translational motion. The rigid movement of an object in a straight line, as opposed to rolling, sliding, and so forth.

Transverse wave. A **wave** whose direction of propagation is perpendicular to the direction of vibration of the medium in which it is travelling. The wave consists of a series of crests and troughs. A **wavelength** is the **distance** between two successive crests or troughs.

Compare to **longitudinal wave**

Tricarboxylic acid (TCA) cycle. See **Krebs cycle**

Tricuspid valve. A leaflet of **tissue** that separates the right **atrium** and right **ventricle**. When open, it allows **blood** to flow only from the atrium to the ventricle.

tRNA. See **transfer ribonucleic acid**

Tropism, viral. The capacity of a **virus** to selectively enter and infect specific **cell** types (e.g., human immunodeficiency virus selectively enters **helper T cells** that express the CD4 surface **molecule**).

Tropomyosin. A long **protein** filament that is woven around the **actin** filament in **sarcomeres**. It blocks the **myosin** binding site on the actin filament until a wave of **depolarization** causes its removal, at which point myosin can bind and **muscle contraction** can occur.

See also **troponin**

Troponin. A regulator **protein** in the **actin** complex of **sarcomeres** that contains calcium **ion** binding sites. Calcium is released when a **muscle fiber** is stimulated by a **nerve impulse**. The binding of calcium to troponin leads to a shift in the position of **tropomyosin**, thus allowing **muscle contraction** to occur.

Tunica adventitia. See **adventitia**

Tunica intima. See **intima**

Tunica media. The middle layer of most **blood vessels**, except capillaries. It is located between the **intima** and **adventitia**. It is made up of modified **smooth muscle cells** and elastic **connective tissue**. Veins generally have fewer layers of smooth muscle cells than arteries do.

Turbulent flow. The irregular flow of a **fluid** that is characterized by the formation of small, erratic whirlpools called "eddies," which create internal **friction** and absorb **energy**.

Compare to **streamline flow**

Tympanic membrane. A barrier that separates the **external ear** from the **middle ear**. Its inward movements, which result from the **pressure** of **sound** waves, cause the movement of the ossicular system in the middle ear.

Also called eardrum

U

Urea. A compound formed from ammonia and carbon dioxide in the **liver** and excreted in the **urine**. It is the principal nitrogenous waste product of **protein** breakdown and represents approximately half of the **solids** in the urine.

Ureter. The tube that carries **urine** from the **kidneys** to the bladder.

Urethra. The tube that carries **urine** from the bladder to the exterior of the body.

Urine. The **liquid** waste extracted from the **blood** by the **kidneys**. It is stored in the bladder until it is eventually expelled through the **urethra**.

Uterus. A hollow, pear-shaped female **organ** in which the **embryo** develops after **fertilization**.

Also called womb

Utricle. Both the utricle and **sacculus** are small cavities in the **vestibular system** (see Appendix A, Figure 13). Each cavity contains a special sensory region, the **macula**, which detects the position of the head with respect to **gravity** and is sensitive to changes in linear **acceleration**. The utricle is important in maintaining equilibrium or "balance" when upright while the sacculus (or saccule) is important in the maintenance of equilibrium when a person is lying down.

Also called utriculus
Compare to **semicircular ducts**

V

Vagina. A muscular tube that leads from the **uterus** to the exterior of the female reproductive system. It receives **sperm**, acts as a channel for **menstrual flow**, and forms part of the birth canal.

Vagus nerve. The most important **nerve** in the **parasympathetic nervous system**. It is a **cranial nerve** that innervates the **heart** and abdominal viscera.

Valence electrons. The **electrons** in the outermost **shell** of an **atom**. The number of valence electrons is an important determinant of the bonding capacity of an atom.

Valence shell electron pair repulsion theory (VSEPR). A theory that explains the different geometric shapes of **molecules** using the assumption that the actual shape is the one that minimizes the repulsion between the pairs of **valence electrons** of the central **atom** of the molecule.

Valency. The strength of an atomic bond.

van der Waals equation. A formula that applies corrections to the **ideal gas law** to account for the deviations from ideal behavior of **gases** at high **pressures** and low **temperatures**:

$$(P + n^2a/V^2)(V - nb) = nRT$$

    P = pressure
    n = number of moles
  a and b = constants
    V = volume
    R = universal gas constant
    T = absolute temperature

The constants depend only on the gas itself. At a given temperature, the measured pressure is slightly lower than that calculated for an ideal gas due to the attractive forces between the **molecules** of the gas. The measured volume that is actually occupied by the gas is slightly larger than the calculated volume of an ideal gas due to the nonzero volume occupied by the gas molecules.

> ✔ You are not responsible for knowing the equation itself; however, it is a good illustration of the degree of deviation of real gases from the ideal gas law.

> *See also* **kinetic molecular theory of gases**

van der Waals forces. Very weak intermolecular **forces** due to a net attraction between the **nucleus** of one **atom** and the **electrons** of another atom. London dispersion and dipole-dipole interactions are types of van der Waals forces.

Vaporization. The conversion of a **liquid** to a **gas** at the **boiling point** without a chemical change.

Vapor pressure. The **pressure** exerted by the vapor of a **liquid** under equilibrium conditions. The vapor pressure is directly related to the **temperature**.

✔ In the case of vapor pressure, the **equilibrium state** is a dynamic equilibrium in which the rate of **evaporation** is equal to the rate of **condensation**.

Vapor pressure lowering (ΔP). A **colligative property** that is the difference between the **vapor pressure** of a pure **solvent** and the vapor pressure of a **solution** using that solvent. It is a positive value because the vapor pressure of the solution is always lower than that of the pure solvent.

Vas deferens. A long tube in the male reproductive system that carries **sperm** from the **epididymis** to the **seminal vesicles**.

Vasoconstriction. A narrowing of the lumen of a **blood vessel** due to the contraction of the **smooth muscle cells** in the vessel walls.

Compare to **vasodilation**

Vasodilation. A widening of the lumen of a **blood vessel** due to the relaxation of the **smooth muscle cells** in the vessel walls.

Compare to **vasoconstriction**

Vasopressin. A **hormone** that is synthesized by the **hypothalamus** and released by the **posterior pituitary gland**. It acts on the **collecting tubule** and **collecting duct** of the **nephron** to promote the reabsorption of water by the **kidney**. It can also induce arteriolar constriction.

Also called antidiuretic hormone

Vector. A quantity or value that has both magnitude and direction.

Compare to **scalar**

Vein. Any **blood vessel** that carries **blood** toward the **heart**. A venule is a small blood vessel that carries blood from the **capillaries** to a vein.

Velocity (V). The **displacement** (*d*) of an object as a function of time (Δt) [a **vector**]. Without the use of calculus, we are limited to the calculation of the average velocity (i.e., the displacement in a given time interval):

$$v = \frac{d}{\Delta t}$$

Vena cava. The largest **vein** in the body. The two divisions of the vena cava, the inferior and superior, both carry **blood** to the right **atrium** of the **heart**.

Ventricle (of the heart). A cavity of the **heart** into which **blood** flows from an **atrium**. The ventricle then propels the blood out of the heart into an **artery**. The right ventricle pumps blood toward the **lungs** via the pulmonary artery; the left ventricle pumps oxygenated blood into **systemic circulation** via the **aorta**.

✔ In general, a ventricle is any cavity in an **organ**.

Vertebrate. A **chordate** that belongs to the subphylum Vertebrata. Vertebrates differ from other chordates in that the **notochord** is ultimately replaced by a bony vertebral column.

Vestibular system. The group of structures in the **inner ear** that function to maintain the positional equilibrium of the body (e.g., posture, balance) [see Appendix A, Figure 13].

Villi. See **intestinal villi**

Viremia. The presence of a **virus** in the **blood**.

Virtual image. An image produced by a **lens** or mirror that does not have light rays actually passing through it and thus cannot be projected onto a screen. However, the human eye interprets the light that enters it as if the rays had originated from a point in front of the lens or mirror that is producing the image. Virtual images correspond to negative image distances ($-i$).

>   *Compare to* **real image**

Virulence. The capacity of a **virus** to produce illness or death.

Virus. An obligate intracellular parasite that consists of a single strand or multiple strands of **nucleic acid** [**deoxyribonucleic acid (DNA)** or **ribonucleic acid (RNA)**] encased in a **protein** coat. A virus can only reproduce by infecting a living host and highjacking its molecular reproductive machinery. Viruses are thought to originate from fragments of DNA or RNA that become detached from bacterial **genomes** or eukaryotic **chromosomes** (see Appendix A, Figure 17).

Viscosity. The internal **friction** of a **fluid** (i.e., the resistance to flow).

Vital capacity. The maximum amount of air that can be expelled from the **lungs** after they initially fill to their full capacity. It is equal to the sum of the **inspiratory reserve volume**, the **tidal volume**, and the **expiratory reserve volume**. Normally, the vital capacity is approximately 4.5 L.

Vitamin. An essential organic substance that cannot be manufactured by the human body. Vitamins are necessary for the metabolic functions of the body.

Vitreous humor. A gelatinous **fluid** that fills the space between the **retina** and the **lens** in the eyeball. It helps to maintain the **pressure** necessary to keep the eyeball distended.

Volt (V). One joule per coulomb (1 J/C).

>   *See also* **potential difference**

W

Wave, mechanical. A disturbance in a medium, caused by the **oscillation** of an object, such that successive particles in the medium vibrate about their individual equilibrium points. A wave has no tangible aspect; it is essentially a transfer of **energy** through a medium. A wave can travel over large **distances**, but the particles of matter through which it travels have zero net **displacements**. A continuous or periodic wave (the type you will most commonly deal with) can be characterized by its constant **velocity** (v), **wavelength** (λ), **frequency** (f), and **amplitude** (A) as well as by the fact that the medium particles vibrate about their equilibrium positions in **simple harmonic motion**. The velocity of a continuous wave is expressed as: $v = \lambda f$.

✔ **Electromagnetic radiation** is a special type of wave that does not exactly fit the previous descriptives; however, the general principle is similar.

See also **longitudinal wave, transverse wave**

Wavelength (λ). The **distance** from crest to crest or trough to trough in a **transverse wave** or from **rarefaction** to rarefaction or **condensation** to condensation in a **longitudinal wave**. It represents the distance between two particles in a medium with the same **displacement**.

Weak acid. An **acid** that does not completely dissociate in aqueous **solution**. The **acidity constant** describes the extent of dissociation for a given acid.

Weak base. A **base** that does not completely dissociate in aqueous **solution**. The **basicity constant** describes the extent of dissociation for a given base.

Weight (w, F$_g$). The **force** that pulls a mass toward Earth due to **gravity** acting on the mass. The weight of a mass can be calculated using the following equation:

$$F_g = mg$$

m = mass
g = acceleration due to gravity $\cong -10$ m/s^2

Compare to **normal force**

White matter. A general term that refers to any bundle of myelinated **axons** in the nervous system. White matter functions as the conducting portion of the brain and spinal cord.

See also **myelin sheath, Schwann cell**
Compare to **gray matter**

Work (W). The result of a **force** being exerted on an object, which causes its **displacement**, as given in the following equations:

$$W = F \times d \text{ or } W = Fd\cos\Theta$$

F = force
d = displacement

In thermodynamics, a work of expansion is done when the volume of a system is changed at a constant **pressure** and can be represented as:

$$W = -P_{ext}\Delta V$$

P_{ext} = constant external pressure
ΔV = change in volume

A work of expansion can be expressed in terms of a change in the **energy** (ΔE) in which it represents a type of energy transfer (i.e., it is not a **state function**):

$$\Delta E = w + q \; or \; \Delta E = \Delta H - w$$

w = work
q = **heat**
ΔH = **enthalpy change**

✔ The unit of work is the joule (J), which is equal to 1 N·m.

Young's modulus (Y). A property of a **solid** that refers to its degree of change in response to **compression** or **tension**. It is a constant of proportionality that directly relates the **stress** $\left(\dfrac{F}{A}\right)$ on an object to the **strain** $\left(\dfrac{\Delta L}{L}\right)$ the object experiences *(Figure 86):*

$$\frac{F}{A} = Y \cdot \left(\frac{\Delta L}{L}\right)$$

F = force
A = area
Y = Young's modulus
ΔL = change in length
L = original length of solid

See also **bulk modulus, shear modulus**

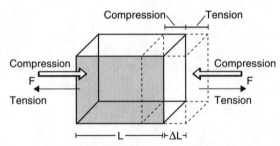

Figure 86. Young's modulus. F = force; L = original length; ΔL = change in length.

Z

Zwitterion. A dipolar (i.e., has two oppositely charged ends) ionic form of a molecule, such as an **amino acid** at neutral **pH** in which the **carboxyl group**(s) have donated their **proton**(s) to the amino groups. *Figure 87* shows the general form of a zwitterion.

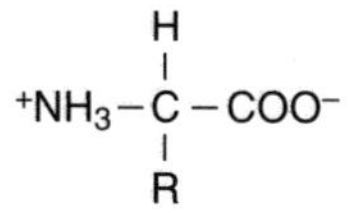

$$^+NH_3 - \overset{\overset{\displaystyle H}{|}}{\underset{\underset{\displaystyle R}{|}}{C}} - COO^-$$

Figure 87. Zwitterion

Zygote. The **diploid cell** that results from the fusion of **sperm** and **ovum** (i.e., **fertilization**). It exists only in the initial stage of **embryogenesis**.

Appendix **A**

ILLUSTRATIONS OF SELECTED BIOLOGY CONCEPTS

Table 1. Comparison of Prokaryotic and Eukaryotic Cells

PROKARYOTES	EUKARYOTES
• Complete absence of nucleus	• Presence of membrane-bound nucleus
• Single, circular DNA strand	• Complex linear chromosomes; DNA conjugated with protein
• No membrane-bound organelles	• Several membrane-bound organelles
• Enzymes are free in cytoplasm	• Subcellular units with specific functions
• Cell wall composed of peptidoglycan (amino sugars and amino acids)	• Cell wall only in plant cells; no cell wall in animal cells
• Small ribosomes free in cytoplasm	• Complex ribosomes bound to rough endoplasmic reticulum
• Always fundamentally single-celled	• Often multicellular organisms
• Division by binary fission	• Division by mitosis; gamete formation by meiosis
• Anaerobic or aerobic metabolism; autotrophic diversity (e.g., N_2 fixation)	• Almost always use aerobic metabolism

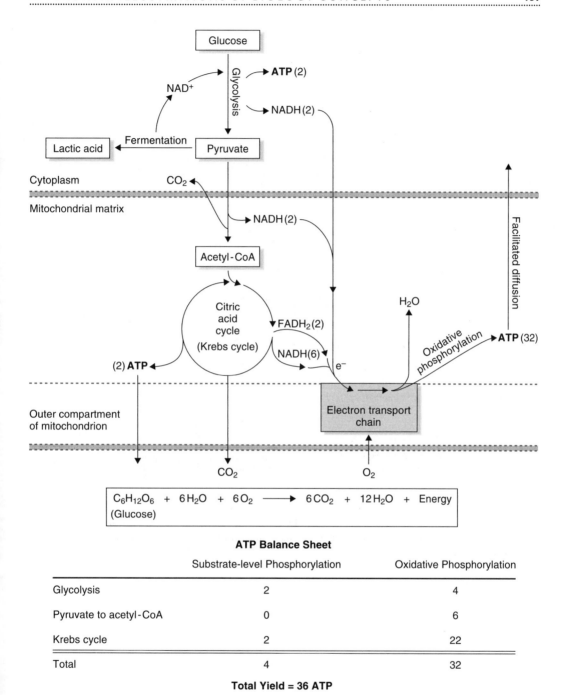

Figure 1. The process of eukaryotic cellular respiration, involving the oxidation of bioorganic molecules. The numbers of ATP and NADH molecules produced are indicated. (See the definition of **cellular respiration** in the glossary for further explanation.) ATP = adenosine triphosphate; CO_2 = carbon dioxide; CoA = coenzyme A; e^- = negative electron; $FADH_2$ = reduced form of flavin adenine dinucleotide; H_2O = water; NAD^+ = oxidized form of nicotinamide adenine dinucleotide; NADH = reduced nicotinamide adenine dinucleotide; O_2 = oxygen.

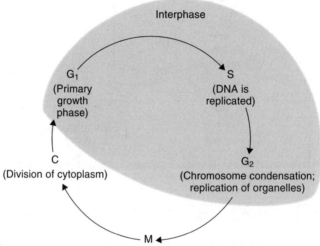

Figure 2. The cell life cycle. G_1 = presynthetic gap; G_2 = postsynthetic gap; C = cytokinesis; M = mitosis; S = synthesis phase.

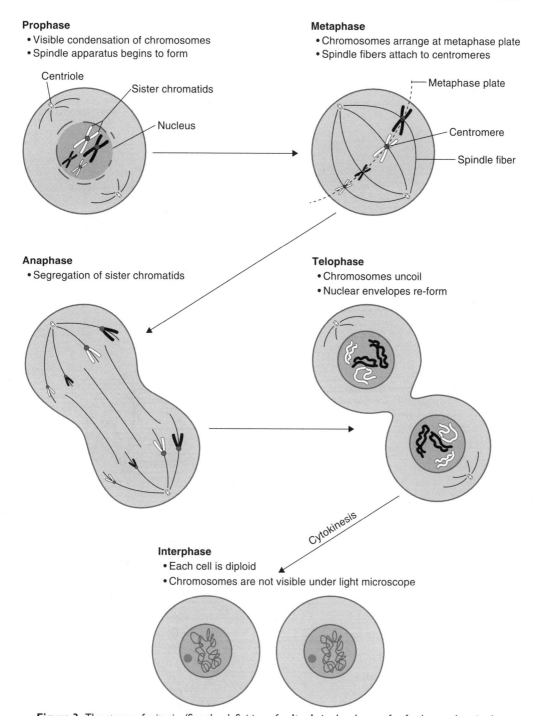

Prophase
- Visible condensation of chromosomes
- Spindle apparatus begins to form

Centriole
Sister chromatids
Nucleus

Metaphase
- Chromosomes arrange at metaphase plate
- Spindle fibers attach to centromeres

Metaphase plate
Centromere
Spindle fiber

Anaphase
- Segregation of sister chromatids

Telophase
- Chromosomes uncoil
- Nuclear envelopes re-form

Cytokinesis

Interphase
- Each cell is diploid
- Chromosomes are not visible under light microscope

Figure 3. The stages of mitosis. (See the definition of **mitosis** in the glossary for further explanation.)

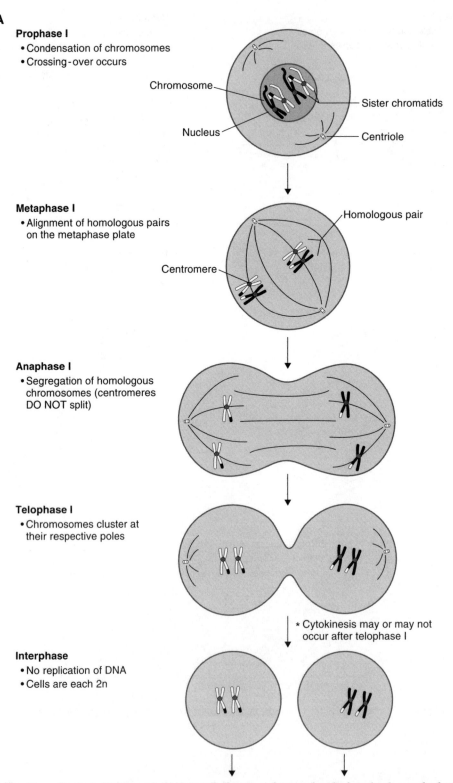

A

Prophase I
- Condensation of chromosomes
- Crossing-over occurs

Chromosome

Sister chromatids

Nucleus

Centriole

Metaphase I
- Alignment of homologous pairs on the metaphase plate

Homologous pair

Centromere

Anaphase I
- Segregation of homologous chromosomes (centromeres DO NOT split)

Telophase I
- Chromosomes cluster at their respective poles

* Cytokinesis may or may not occur after telophase I

Interphase
- No replication of DNA
- Cells are each 2n

Figure 4. The stages of meiosis. (*A*) Meiosis I. (*B*) Meiosis II. (See the definition of **meiosis** in the glossary for further explanation.)

B

Prophase II
- Recondensation of chromosomes
- Spindle apparatus begins to form

Metaphase II
- Chromosomes arrange at metaphase plate
- Spindle fibers attach to centromeres

Anaphase II
- Segregation of sister chromatids

Telophase II
- Chromosomes uncoil
- Nuclear envelopes re-form

Interphase
- Each cell is haploid

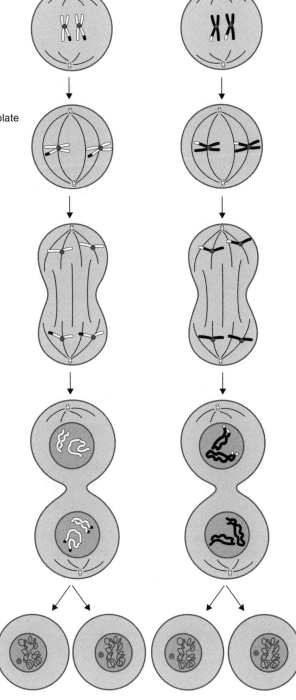

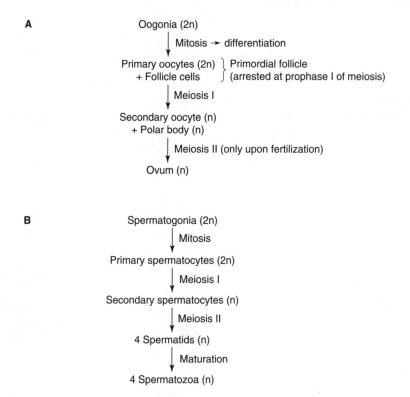

Figure 5. (*A*) Oogenesis: gametogenesis in the female. (*B*) Spermatogenesis: gametogenesis in the male. (See the definition of **spermatogenesis** in the glossary for further explanation.) n = haploid chromosome number.

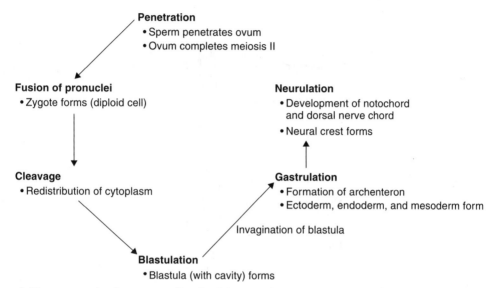

Figure 6. The process of embryogenesis. (See the definitions of **blastula, embryogenesis, gastrula,** and **neurulation** in the glossary for further explanation.)

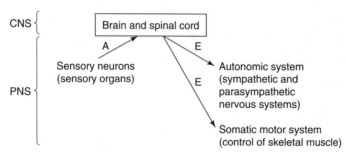

Figure 7. Organization of the vertebrate nervous system. A = afferent pathway; CNS = central nervous system; E = efferent pathway; PNS = peripheral nervous system.

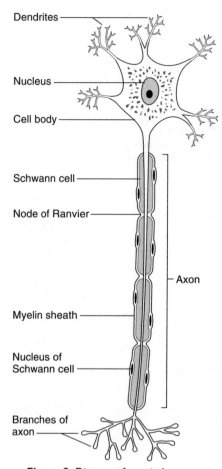

Figure 8. Diagram of a typical neuron.

Hindbrain
  Cerebellum (coordination, balance)
  Pons (relay functions)
  Medulla oblongata (respiration, circulation)

Midbrain (relay functions)

Forebrain
  Hypothalamus (homeostasis, behavior)
  Thalamus (relay center for sensory input)
  Cerebral hemispheres (integration and interpretation, mostly in the cerebral
    cortex)

Figure 9. Parts of the brain. (Also see Figure 10 in Appendix A.) [See the definition of **brain** in the glossary for further explanation.)

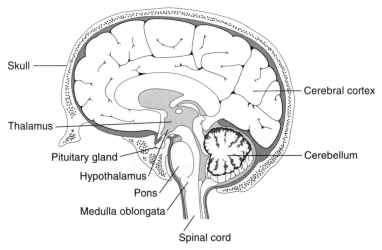

Skull

Cerebral cortex

Thalamus

Pituitary gland

Hypothalamus

Pons

Medulla oblongata

Cerebellum

Spinal cord

Figure 10. A midsagittal section through the brain.

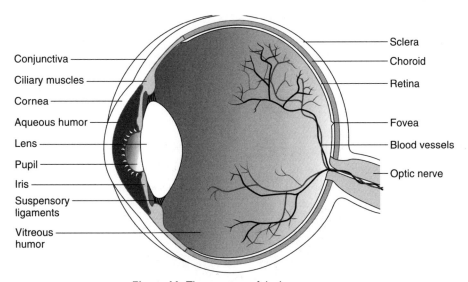

Conjunctiva

Ciliary muscles

Cornea

Aqueous humor

Lens

Pupil

Iris

Suspensory ligaments

Vitreous humor

Sclera

Choroid

Retina

Fovea

Blood vessels

Optic nerve

Figure 11. The structure of the human eye.

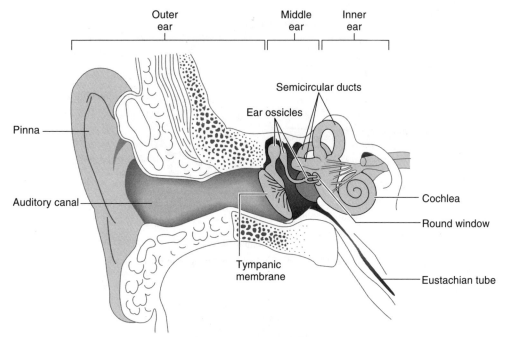

Figure 12. The structure of the human ear.

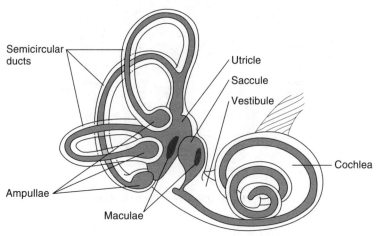

Figure 13. The structure of the inner ear.

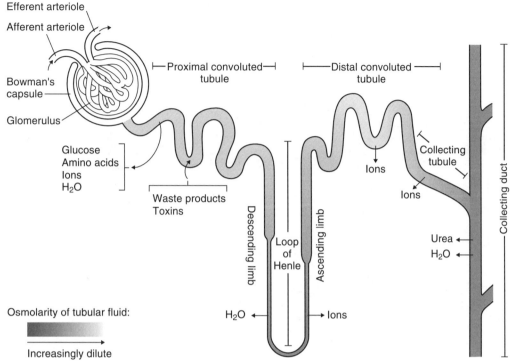

Figure 14. The flow of materials in the human kidney. Each part of the nephron differs in terms of its water permeability: The proximal convoluted tubule and descending limb of the loop of Henle are highly permeable, the ascending limb of the loop of Henle and the distal convoluted tubule are impermeable, and the collecting tubule and duct are variably permeable due to the effects of antidiuretic hormone and aldosterone. (See the definition of **nephron** in the glossary for further explanation.) H_2O = water.

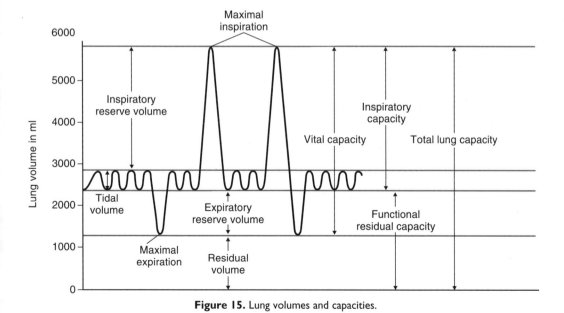

Figure 15. Lung volumes and capacities.

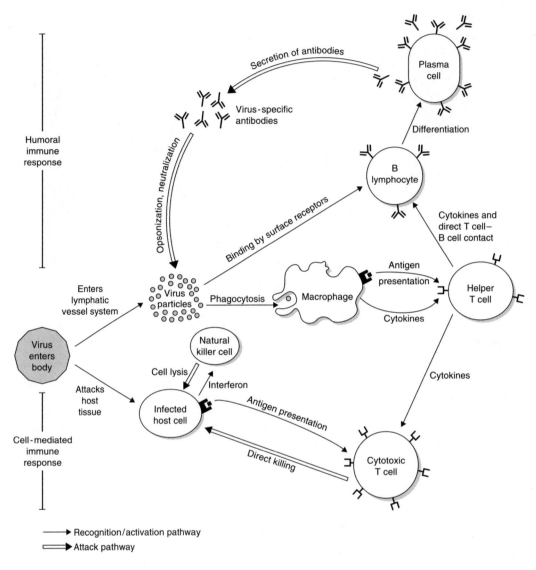

Figure 16. The immune response to a viral pathogen. (See the definition of **immune response** in the glossary for further explanation.)

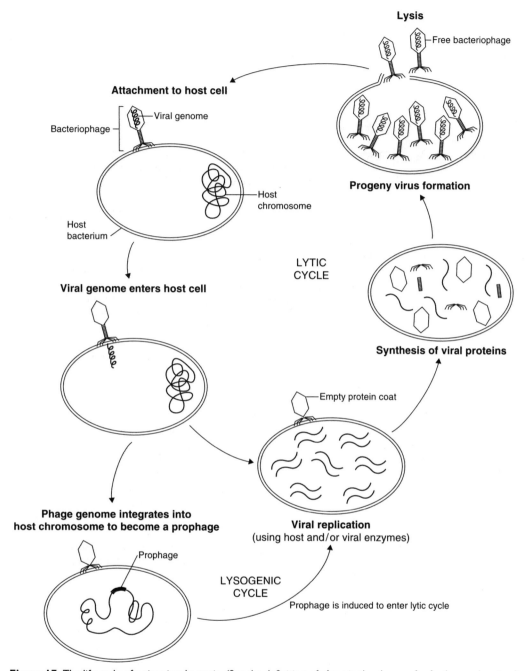

Figure 17. The life cycle of a virus in a bacteria. (See the definition of **virus** in the glossary for further explanation.)

Table 2. Major Hormones

HORMONE	SOURCE GLAND	TARGET ORGAN/TISSUE	ACTION
Adrenaline	Adrenal medulla	Skeletal, smooth, and cardiac muscle	Initiates stress responses (e.g., increase in heart rate, dilation of blood vessels, increase in blood glucose level)
ACTH	Anterior pituitary gland	Adrenal cortex	Stimulates secretion of aldosterone and cortisol
Aldosterone	Adrenal cortex	Collecting tubule and duct of kidney nephrons	Stimulates increased reabsorption (i.e., retention) of sodium ions
ADH (vasopressin)	Hypothalamus; secreted by the posterior pituitary gland	Collecting tubule and duct of kidney nephrons, blood vessels	Stimulates the reabsorption (i.e., retention) of water; may cause vasoconstriction
Calcitonin	Thyroid gland	Bone	Inhibits the loss of calcium from bones
Estrogen	Ovaries	Female genital and reproductive structures	Inhibits FSH production; stimulates the proliferation of the endometrium; triggers the release of LH; maintains female secondary sex characteristics
FSH	Anterior pituitary gland	Reproductive organs	Females: stimulates the growth and secretion of the ovarian follicles Males: stimulates spermatogenesis in the testes
Glucagon	Islets of Langerhans (in the pancreas)	Liver and adipose tissue (fat cells)	Stimulates the breakdown of glycogen and fat
Insulin	Islets of Langerhans (in the pancreas)	Most tissues	Promotes the cellular uptake of glucose; stimulates the formation of glycogen and fat
LH	Anterior pituitary gland	Reproductive organs	Females: stimulates ovulation and the transformation of the ovarian follicle into the corpus luteum Males: stimulates the secretion of testosterone by the interstitial cells of the testes
Oxytocin	Hypothalamus; secreted by the posterior pituitary gland	Uterus, mammary glands	Females: stimulates contractions of the uterus during labor and lactation (ejection of milk) Males: no known function
Parathyroid hormone	Parathyroid glands	Bone, kidneys, digestive tract	Causes increased blood calcium levels by stimulating bone breakdown and calcium reabsorption in the kidneys
Progesterone	Ovaries	Uterus, breasts	Completes the preparation of the uterus for pregnancy; stimulates breast development
Prolactin	Anterior pituitary gland	Mammary glands	Stimulates milk production
GH (somatotropin)	Anterior pituitary gland	Most tissues	Stimulates growth of all organs by the promotion of protein synthesis and breakdown of fatty acids

Table 2. Major Hormones (continued)

HORMONE	SOURCE GLAND	TARGET ORGAN/TISSUE	ACTION
Testosterone	Testes	Male reproductive structures	Stimulates spermatogenesis and the development of secondary male sex characteristics
TSH	Anterior pituitary gland	Thyroid gland	Stimulates the growth of the thyroid gland; induces the secretion of thyroxine
Thyroxine	Thyroid gland	Most tissues	Stimulates an increase in the rate of energy use by the body

ACTH = adrenocorticotropic hormone; ADH = antidiuretic hormone; FSH = follicle-stimulating hormone; GH = growth hormone; LH = luteinizing hormone; TSH = thyroid-stimulating hormone.

Table 3. Major Macromolecules

MACROMOLECULE	SUBUNIT	FUNCTION
Carbohydrates		
Glycogen	Glucose	Energy storage in animals
Starch	Glucose	Energy storage in plants
Lipids		
Fats	Glycerol + 3 fatty acids	Long-term energy storage
Phospholipids	Glycerol + 2 fatty acids + phosphate	Plasma membrane bilayer
Steroids	Four-carbon rings	Hormones; plasma membrane fluidity
Proteins	Amino acids	Biochemical catalysis; transport; structure
Nucleic Acids		
DNA	Deoxyribonucleotides	Genetic code
RNA	Ribonucleotides	Various gene expression functions

Appendix **B**

ILLUSTRATIONS OF SELECTED CHEMISTRY CONCEPTS

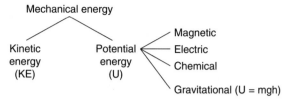

Figure 1. The types of energy classified as mechanical energy. g = acceleration due to gravity; h = height of body; m = mass of body.

A

$Q = C \cdot m \cdot \Delta t$
Q = heat exchanged
C = specific heat
m = mass of body/object
Δt = change in temperature

B

$\Delta E = q - w; \Delta E = q - P\Delta V$
$\therefore$ When $\Delta V = 0$, $\Delta E = q_v$
and when $\Delta P = 0$, $\Delta H = q_p$
ΔE = change in energy
q = heat
w = work
P = pressure
ΔV = change in volume
q_v = heat at constant volume
ΔP = change in pressure
ΔH = enthalpy change
q_p = heat at constant pressure

C

$\Delta S = \dfrac{q_{rev}}{T}$
$\Delta S_{total} = \Delta S_{system} + \Delta S_{surroundings} < 0$
$W_{rev} < W_{irrev}$
$q_{rev} < q_{irrev}$
ΔS = change in entropy
q_{rev} = heat of reversible process
T = temperature
W_{rev} = work by reversible process
W_{irrev} = work by irreversible process
q_{irrev} = heat of irreversible process

D

$\Delta G = \Delta H - T\Delta S$
$(\Delta G = q_{irrev} - q_{rev})$
ΔG = change in free energy
ΔH = enthalpy change
T = temperature
ΔS = change in entropy
q_{irrev} = heat of irreversible process
q_{rev} = heat of reversible process

E

$\Delta H^\circ_f = \Sigma \Delta H^\circ_f \text{ (products)} - \Sigma \Delta H^\circ_f \text{ (reactants)}$
ΔH°_f = heat of formation
Σ = summation sign

Figure 2. Various formulas related to thermodynamics. (A) Specific heat. (B) Changes in energy and enthalpy. (C) Entropy. (D) Free energy. (E) Hess's law.

A

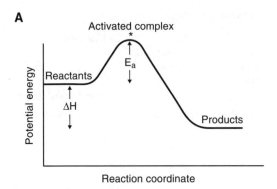

Rate = K [A]^m [B]^n...

B

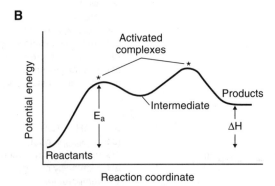

Figure 3. Chemical kinetics. (*A*) **Exothermic reaction.** The potential energy of the products is lower than that of the reactants; therefore, the products have lower energy bonds. (*B*) **Endothermic reaction.** The potential energy of the products is higher than that of the reactants; therefore, the products have higher energy bonds. Less energy is released upon formation of the new bonds than was initially required to break the old bonds. Intermediates can be isolated. (See the definitions of **activation energy** and **enthalpy change** in the glossary for futher explanation.) E_a = activation energy; ΔH = enthalpy change; K = rate constant; [A] = initial concentration of reactant A; [B] = initial concentration of reactant B; m and n = experimentally-determined exponents.

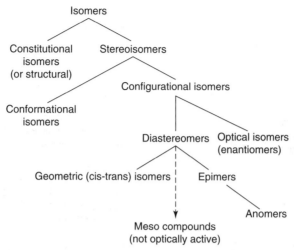

Figure 4. A diagram illustrating the different types of isomers.

A

$$HA + H_2O \rightleftharpoons H_3O^+ + A^-$$

$$K_a = \frac{[A^-][H_3O^+]}{[HA]}$$

A = weak acid
K_a = acidity constant

B

$$B + H_2O \rightleftharpoons BH^+ + OH^-$$

$$K_b = K_h = \frac{[OH^-][BH^+]}{[B]}$$

B = weak base
K_b = basicity constant

C

$$pH = -log[H_3O^+]; pOH = -log[OH^-]$$
$$pH + pOH = 14 = pK_w$$
$$K_w = [H^+][OH^-] = 1 \times 10^{-14}$$
$$pK_w = -logK_w$$

K_w = equilibrium constant for the dissociation of water

D

$$pH = pK_a + log\left(\frac{[A^-]}{[HA]}\right)$$

$pK_a = -logK_a$
A = weak acid
K_a = acidity constant

Figure 5. Formulas associated with acids and bases. (A) Weak acid dissociation. (B) Weak base protonation (hydrolysis). (C) pH scale. (D) Buffers (Henderson-Hasselbach formula). (See the definitions of **acidity constant** and **basicity constant** in the glossary for further explanation.)

A

$PV = nRT$

$\left(P + \dfrac{n^2a}{V^2}\right)(V - nb) = nRT$

P = pressure
V = volume
n = number of moles
R = universal gas constant
T = absolute temperature
a and b = constants with values that
depend solely on the gas itself

B

$P_{Total} = P_1 + P_2 + P_3 + \cdots + P_i = \sum_i P_i$

$P_i = X_i P_{Total}$, where $X_i = \dfrac{n_i}{n_{Total}}$

P_{Total} = total pressure
$\sum_i P_i$ = sum of all individual partial pressures
X_i = mole fraction of component i
n_i = number of moles of component i
n_{Total} = total number of moles

C

$PV = \frac{2}{3}NE_K$

E_K (per mole) $= \frac{3}{2}RT$

$v_{rms} = \sqrt{\dfrac{3RT}{M}}$

$\dfrac{\text{rate of effusion of gas 1}}{\text{rate of effusion of gas 2}} = \dfrac{\sqrt{M_2}}{\sqrt{M_1}}$

(Graham's law of effusion)

P = pressure
v = volume
N = number of moles
E_K = translational kinetic energy per mole
R = universal gas constant
T = temperature
V_{rms} = root-mean-square speed
M = molar weight

D

$C_V = \frac{3}{2}R = 12.5 \text{ J/mol} \cdot \text{K}$
(for monoatomic gases)
$\Delta KE = nC_V\Delta T$
$Q = nC_P\Delta T$
$C_P - C_V = R$
C_V = heat capacity at constant volume
R = universal gas constant
ΔKE = change in kinetic energy
n = number of moles
ΔT = change in temperature
Q = heat
C_P = heat capacity at constant pressure

Figure 6. Gas laws. (*A*) Ideal gas law and Van der Waal's equation. (*B*) Partial pressures. (*C*) Kinetics. (*D*) Thermodynamics.

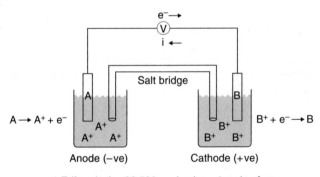

1 F (faraday) = 96,500 coulombs = 1 mole of e^-

Figure 7. An electrochemical cell. (See the definition of **electrochemical cell** in the glossary for futher explanation.) e^- = electron; i = current; V = voltage.

Appendix **C**

COMMON PHYSICS FORMULAS

A

F = ma
F = force
m = mass of body/object
a = acceleration

B

W = Fdcosθ
W = work
F = force
d = displacement

C

KE = $\frac{1}{2}$mv^2
KE = kinetic energy
m = mass of body/object
v = velocity

D

U = mgh
U = potential energy
m = mass of body/object
g = acceleration due to gravity
h = height of body/object

Figure 1. Formulas associated with dynamics. (A) Force. (B) Work. (C) Kinetic energy. (D) Potential energy.

$$\mathbf{d = d_o + v_o t + \tfrac{1}{2} at^2 \text{ or } d = d_o + v_o t + \tfrac{1}{2} gt^2}$$

A

$v_y 0 = v_o \sin\theta$

B

$y = v_y ot + \frac{1}{2} gt^2$

C

$v_y = v_y 0 + gt$

D

$v^2{}_y = v^2{}_y 0 + 2gy$

E

$v_{xo} = v_o \cos\theta$

F

$x = v_{xo}\, t$

G

$v_x = v_{xo}$

Figure 2. Formulas associated with kinematics and projectile motion. Using the initial formulas, A–G can be derived. (A) Vertical component of initial velocity v_o. (B) Vertical displacement at time t. (C) Vertical velocity at time t. (D) Vertical velocity at height y. (E) Horizontal component of initial velocity v_o. (F) Horizontal displacement at time t. (G) Horizontal velocity (a constant). (See the definition of **projectile motion** in the glossary for further explanation.) g = acceleration due to gravity $\cong -10$ m/s^2.

$$\mathbf{F = \frac{\Delta p}{\Delta t}} \text{ or } \mathbf{p = mv}$$

F = force
Δp = impulse
Δt = duration of time
p = linear momentum
m = mass of object
v = velocity

Figure 3. Newton's second law, used to calculate linear momentum.

A

$$F = k\frac{Q_1Q_2}{r^2}$$

F = electrostatic force
$k \cong 9 \times 10^9$ N · m²/c² (a constant)
Q = magnitude of charge (in coulombs)
r = distance between the two charges

B

$$E = \frac{F}{q} = k\frac{Q}{r^2}$$

E = electric field
F = electrostatic force
q = positive test charge
$k \cong 9 \times 10^9$ N · m²/c² (a constant)
Q = point charge
r = distance from point charge

C

$$\mu = qd$$

μ = dipole moment
q = magnitude of single charge
d = disance between opposite charges

D

$$V = \frac{W}{q}; PE = qV = W$$

V = electric potential
W = work
q = electric charge
PE = potential energy

E

$$V = Ed$$

V = potential difference
E = magnitude of uniform electric field
d = distance between given points in electric field

Figure 4. Formulas associated with electrostatics. (A) Electrostatic force. (B) Electric field. (C) Dipole moment. (D) Electric potential. (E) Potential difference.

A

$$F_B = qvBsin\theta$$

F_B = magnetic force
q = magnitude of the charge
v = velocity of the charge
B = magnitude of the magnetic field

B

$$F_B = iLBsin\theta$$

F_B = magnetic force
i = current
L = length of the wire
B = magnitude of the magnetic field

Figure 5. Formulas associated with electromagnetism. (A) Magnetic force (use right hand rule #2). (B) Force on a current-carrying wire.

A

$$V = iR$$

V = voltage
i = current
R = resistance

B

$$\rho = \frac{RA}{L}$$

ρ = resistivity
R = resistance
A = cross-sectional area of wire
L = length of wire

C

$$Q = CV$$

Q = charge on each plate
C = capacitance
V = potential difference between the two plates

D

$$P = Vi = i^2R = \frac{V^2}{R}$$

P = power
V = voltage
i = current
R = resistance

Figure 6. Formulas associated with electricity. (A) Ohm's law. (B) Resistivity. (C) Capacitance. (D) Power.

A

$$v = \lambda f; \quad f = \frac{1}{T}$$

v = velocity
f = frequency
T = period

B

$$E_{photon} = hf$$

E_{photon} = energy of a single photon
h = Planck's constant $\cong 6.6 \times 10^{-34}$ J · s
f = frequency of wave

C

$$I \propto A^2 f^2$$

I = intensity of wave (in watts/meter^2)
A = amplitude
f = frequency

D

$$\beta = 10 \log \left(\frac{I}{I_o}\right)$$

β = sound level (in decibels)
I = intensity of sound wave
I_o = standard reference intensity
(usually 1.0×10^{-12} watts/meter^2)

E

$$F = -kx$$

F = restoring force
k = spring constant
x = change in length of the spring from
its equilibrium position

F

$$f' = f\left(\frac{v \pm v_d}{v \mp v_s}\right)$$

f' = observed frequency
f = frequency of the wave at the source
v = velocity of the wave
v_d = velocity of the detector
v_s = velocity of the source

Figure 7. Formulas applied to waves. (A) General formulas. (B) Electromagnetic radiation. (C) Intensity. (D) Sound level. (E) Hooke's law. (F) Doppler effect.

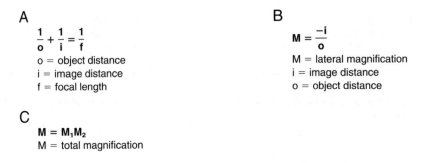

A

$$\frac{1}{o} + \frac{1}{i} = \frac{1}{f}$$

o = object distance
i = image distance
f = focal length

B

$$M = \frac{-i}{o}$$

M = lateral magnification
i = image distance
o = object distance

C

$$M = M_1 M_2$$

M = total magnification

Figure 8. Formulas associated with optics. (A) Lens/mirror equation. (B) Lateral magnification. (C) Magnification with two lenses.

A

$P = \rho gh$
P = pressure of the fluid
ρ = density of the fluid
g = acceleration due to gravity
h = depth below the surface of the fluid

B

$F_b = V\rho g = mg$
F_b = buoyant force
V = volume of fluid displaced by floating object
ρ = density of fluid
g = acceleration due to gravity
m = mass of fluid of volume V

C

$P + \rho gh + \frac{1}{2}\rho v^2 = $ constant
P = pressure of the fluid
ρ = density of the fluid
g = acceleration due to gravity
h = height of fluid above a reference level
v = velocity of the fluid

D

$Av = $ constant
ρAv = constant (conservation of mass)
A = area through which fluid passes
v = velocity of flow
ρ = density of the fluid

E

Turbulence $\propto v \cdot d$
v = velocity of the fluid
d = diameter of the channel through which the fluid is flowing

Figure 9. Formulas applied to fluids. (*A*) Pressure. (*B*) Archimedes principle. (*C*) Bernoulli's theorem. (*D*) Continuity equation. (*E*) Viscosity.

Stress = modulus × strain

A

$$\frac{F}{A} = Y\left(\frac{\Delta L}{L}\right)$$
F = force
A = area
Y = Young's modulus
ΔL = change in length
L = original length of solid

B

$$\frac{F}{A} = G\left(\frac{\Delta L}{L_o}\right)$$
F = force
A = area
G = shear modulus
ΔL = change in length
L_o = height of object

C

$$P = B\left(\frac{\Delta V}{V}\right)$$
P = pressure of surrounding fluid
B = bulk modulus
ΔV = change in volume
V = initial volume

Figure 10. Formulas associated with elasticity. (*A*) Compression and tension. (*B*) Shear stress. (*C*) Hydraulic compression.